DIALOGUE IN MEDICINE AND THEOLOGY

DIALOGUE IN MEDICINE AND THEOLOGY

EDITED BY DALE WHITE

ABINGDON PRESS Nashville and New York

DIALOGUE IN MEDICINE AND THEOLOGY

Library of Congress Catalog Card Number: 68-17450

SET UP, PRINTED, AND BOUND BY THE PARTHENON PRESS, AT NASHVILLE, TENNESSEE, UNITED STATES OF AMERICA good enough in its day, but now that we see human life as a whole, we recognize that its treatment must be whole. The solution to moral evil can be approached by the psychiatrist; physical disorder may be eased by the minister.

From the old point of view the pastor who came to counsel and pray with a member before an operation was performing a sacred duty. The surgeon who subsequently operated on this patient was performing a secular duty. Yet it is the same body and the same person, and it is the wholeness of this person which is involved. Now we see that minister and surgeon alike may be thought of as doing sacred tasks. This involves us not only in mutual respect but a recognition of mutual responsibilities. It brings medicine and theology together in dealing with a human being. It brings them together in facing moral issues which arise in the consideration of differing human problems. It is in the light of this that the Convocation on Medicine and Theology was conceived and for which the following call was given to the church:

"Because of the common ground shared by the disciplines of theology and medicine, and the common ministry in services to the whole man, we call physicians, pastors, chaplains, administrators in hospitals and homes for aging, medical social workers, nurses and specialists in pastoral counseling, to a Convocation on Medicine and Theology. The meeting is scheduled for April 5-7, 1967, at Mayo Clinic and Rochester Methodist Hospital, Rochester, Minnesota, under the sponsorship of the Board of Hospitals and Homes, the Board of Christian Social Concerns, the Board of Missions, and the Commission on Chaplains of The Methodist Church.

"We are glad to see Methodism pioneering in this venture.

INTRODUCTION

This is a great age in which to live so long as we are willing to become excited about the great issues which confront us. New ideas frighten many persons and make them yearn for the old world of comfortable, familiar ways.

One of the fascinating new areas of thought is the advocacy of new definitions of the sacred and the secular. We see this on the one hand in the appeal to understand that religion is not just what takes place in a sanctuary on a Sunday morning or in weekday programs and meetings in the church building. The new emphasis asks us to see that religion is related to all of life and that we cannot be partial Christians.

Perhaps nowhere is this better seen than in the human body. It is the seat of moral evil and of physical disease. Traditionally we have supposed that the clergyman attacked evil and the physician attacked disease. This may have been

Recognizing that God heals and men are his servants in the healing process, we note the purpose of the Convocation:

"To explore ways in which individual Christians in the professional disciplines of the churches and medicine may work together to accomplish the maximum in the treatment of the whole person;

"To share the concern and conviction that men of both medicine and theology are men of religion and have, therefore, a common purpose and goal in the healing process;

"To deepen the understanding and foster the acceptance of the disciplines of each profession by providing the context for honest dialogue and personal confrontation;

"To seek ways in which each Methodist-related hospital, center for service to older persons and child care may become an effective setting and a unique Christian context in which the treatment team may establish and fulfill its highest scientific, spiritual, and socio-psychological levels demanded by our involvement in the Christian faith."

The papers read were received by the delegates, physicians and clergy alike, with high enthusiasm. The delegates agreed immediately that these papers should be printed, so that their importance could be shared by a larger group of interested persons.

FRED G. HOLLOWAY
A Retired Bishop
of The United Methodist Church

Let a degree of exaggeration be admitted in this definition of society's hostility toward the physician and the clergyman. Yet in the deflated residuum we have abundant justification for concern and sufficient stimulus to seek society's reasons for hostile displays. That a single element will be found responsible for the generation of society's hostility toward the two professions is a likely outcome of any analysis of this hostility. Ironically enough, that common element may be defined as the comparative security and freedom from the ravages of disease and destruction which are the seeming good fortune of present-day affluent American society. Let us pursue this analysis, then, as it pertains to the physician on the one hand and the clergyman on the other.

The early-twentieth-century physician had at his command few specific measures of medical treatment. He had neither effective drugs nor effective dietary and rehabilitation programs, nor did he have effective surgical procedures. Given his choice between a patient with an infectious disease such as pneumonia or a metabolic disease such as diabetes on the one hand, and a patient with migraine or a nervous stomach on the other, he would choose the latter patient, because at least within the means at his command he could keep the afflicted one alive, and might even effect improvement in the patient's symptoms by the simple process of counsel and understanding.

Today's physician can with drugs alone predictably and totally cure the majority of infectious diseases and can manage skillfully any but the most catastrophic metabolic ailments. Understandably, then, he is able to satisfy both his patient and himself when the opportunity comes to treat

PREFACE

The primary purpose of the Convocation on Medicine and Theology which gave rise to this volume was more and better communication between physicians and clergymen. This specific effort to promote dialogue between the two professions—and there are many others like it—does not necessarily imply a kindling of affection between physician and clergyman, any more than the limited communications of the past bespoke hostility and estrangement. The two professions seek this new intimacy for reasons which derive more from pragmatism than from altruism. Mutually and profoundly they have come to know how much they need to understand one another if they are to defend themselves adequately against charges which an aroused society directs almost indiscriminately against one or the other. This search for understanding is not exclusively defensive, and certainly we may anticipate its consequences will have more to do with production of a greater good than with resistance of a common opponent.

these serious organic diseases. On the other hand, he is probably no more effective than his predecessor of half a century ago in the treatment of migraine and nervous indigestion. Recognition of his success in treating organic disease only serves to intensify his own frustration in the management of the patient with functional disease, and this intensified frustration is reflected in his conduct. He gives less and less time and becomes more and more irascible in his care of the patient with psychosomatic problems. And since the successful management of the organically ill eliminates them as a public voice, only the functionally ill remain to raise louder and louder cry against the physician's aloofness and lack of compassion, and to recall nostalgically the horse-and-buggy doctor who really cured nothing but patiently dealt with his frustrations in the treatment of all categories of illness, organic or functional.

Likewise the clergyman finds that the members of society, protected and reasonably secure, become less and less interested in and dependent upon religion throughout the long periods of quiet and comfort. But ultimately they come alive with intensified hostility toward the catastrophies that inevitably beset life, whether those tragedies be in the form of physical destruction or emotional crisis. The clergyman finds himself annoyed with the indifference of the untroubled multitudes and the frenzied hostility of the scattered few who have come belatedly to recognize that even with the best of luck and the finest of social and medical protections, the day of organic and emotional dissolution eventually comes upon them.

Many would not support, and a few would not even condone, this emphasis upon response to a common enemy as the dominant conditioner in the efforts of physician and clergyman each better to understand the other. Perhaps I have elected preeminence for this motivation just to make perfectly certain none of us gets too smug and too holy about his reasons for assiduous participation in so noble an effort. For this is a noble effort, and whatever may be the reasons why we, physicians and clergymen, have come together, we do indeed have hard work to do and loads to lift.

But we have more than a burden to bear. We have a noble heritage to honor and a shining destiny to fulfill. Certainly there are ills which appear solely organic and the solitary domain of the physician, and others which are seemingly without physical and material components and primarily in the realm of the clergyman. But between the two extremes is the vast range of human affliction composed of highly specific aliquots affecting body, mind, and spirit. Even to identify the degree to which each of these three elements participates in a given illness is difficult, and their separation one from the other is impossible. Human illness traced back to its source in the individual patient almost inevitably provides a meeting place for the physician and the clergyman and a bright and challenging opportunity for the best efforts of both, one in support of the other. Communion between the ministry of healing and the ministry of faith is as old as man's search for God in the turmoil of lives beset by the malignancies of passions and plagues, of demons and death. All reason, then, that the physician and the clergyman should join in devout chorus with Charles Wesley:

> Almighty God of truth and love,
> To me thy power impart;

PREFACE

The burden from my soul remove,
  The hardness from my heart.
O may the least omission pain
  My reawakened soul,
And drive me to that grace again,
  Which makes the wounded whole.

RAYMOND D. PRUITT, M.D.
Chairman of the Department of Medicine
Baylor School of Medicine
Houston, Texas

CONTRIBUTORS

FRANCIS J. BRACELAND, M.D., Professor of Psychiatry, Yale University; Senior Consultant of the Institute of Living, Hartford, Connecticut; Editor, *American Journal of Psychiatry.*

MELVIN A. CASBERG, M.D., Harriman Jones Medical Clinic, Long Beach, California.

HOWARD J. CLINEBELL, JR., PH.D., Professor of Pastoral Theology, the School of Theology at Claremont, Claremont, California.

JOSEPH FLETCHER, PH.D., Professor of Pastoral Theology and Christian Ethics, Episcopal Theological Seminary, Cambridge, Massachusetts.

SEWARD HILTNER, PH.D., Professor of Theology and Personality, Princeton Theological Seminary.

Amos N. Johnson, M.D., Garland, North Carolina; President of the Academy of General Practice.

Edward M. Litin, M.D., Head of the Section of Psychiatry, Mayo Clinic, Rochester, Minnesota.

J. Robert Nelson, Ph.D., Professor of Systematic Theology, Boston University School of Theology.

Roy Nichols, Ph.D., Pastor, Salem Methodist Church, New York, New York.

Raymond D. Pruitt, M.D., Chairman of the Department of Medicine, Baylor School of Medicine, Houston, Texas.

Edward H. Rynearson, M.D., Emeritus Consultant in Internal Medicine, Mayo Clinic, Rochester, Minnesota.

CONTENTS

I. Contributions of Medicine and Theology to the Health of Man: A Dialogue

Francis J. Braceland and J. Robert Nelson

Francis J. Braceland

This Convocation on Medicine and Theology is timely, for there is unrest in the land. While on one hand the spirit of ecumenism is evident, on the other we are notified solemnly that God is dead. In our everyday life we read about men who die gloriously on the battlefield to save their friends and fellow men, while at home they are unable to live peaceably beside one another. One could, without procrustean effort, paraphrase Dickens in his *Tale of Two Cities,* for it seems singularly apropos: "These are the best of times, they are the worst of times; it is the epoch of belief and it is the epoch of incredulity. . . . It is the season of light and the season of darkness. We are all going direct to heaven, we are all going direct the other way."

The click that we hear, however, is not Madame DeFarge's needles but rather that of electronic devices as they measure radioactive fall-out and record far-off nuclear explosions.

Despite all unrest and change, however, the historic tasks of physicians and clergymen remain essentially the same as they were a century ago—with one new bit of insight. Doctors and ministers realize now that they need each other. This convocation is recognition of that fact. The American Medical Association's Medicine and Religion program, founded in

1961, is another. According to an official notice, there are today 48 state and 622 county medical society Medicine and Religion committees, and the program is a going concern. All of this is so, not only because in its long history medicine has shown a sensitivity to the moral dimension of its practices, but because what is different today is that in a special way medicine has become everyone's business.[1] This increased interest is due to the spectacular successes achieved by modern medicine, successes reported to laymen in virtually all mass communications media.

I am sure, however, you do not require of me a long recital of medicine's spectacular successes in the health field, or failures either. It is probable that you require something more in keeping with the purpose outlined in the call for the convocation. First, we might speak of the positions in which clergymen and physicians find themselves today, for there is some disquiet in both groups. Then we might consider the hospital, the usual meeting place for patient, physician, and clergyman. Finally, it would be profitable to turn our attention to medicine in general, for it has provoked some serious moral questions, "not through perversity, but because of the enormous momentum medical science has gained in the past few decades." [2] The office of medicine, Francis Bacon said, "is but to tune this curious harp of man's body and reduce it to harmony." Almost four centuries later, in the accelerating scientific revolution, medicine is doing the tuning but is having trouble with the harmony.

[1] Samuel E. Stumpf, in *Annals of Internal Medicine,* February, 1966.
[2] *Ibid.*

Disquiet Among Physicians and Clergy

Theologians now are busy about many things, and are presently required to reassess positions once thought settled beyond a doubt but which now are being challenged by their own brethren, clerical and lay. Biblical scholars of various denominations are uniting their labors in further study of the Scriptures, and an ecumenical effort to collaborate for the common good is everywhere apparent. There have always been tensions in the church. Even the apostles had their differences. Take the friction between the progressive Paul and the conservative James, both holy men. Despite the differences, however, as one scholar says, "we should not go around trying to excommunicate one another; we should open our eyes and look for opportunities to bear witness."

Physicians, for their part, are unhappy about present-day medical education and some aspects of today's medical practice. As the culmination of an information explosion in the basic sciences over a period of several decades, the profession has been pushed to an extreme of specialization, while various sociologic changes and government involvement have necessitated changes in medical practice. While the individual doctor is still held in high regard, medicine in general has slipped a notch in the affections of the people. All the recent legislation, which literally will change the practice of medicine, was passed without as much as a "by your leave" of the doctors.

Though the present-day doctor is much more highly trained and more scientific than ever before, it seems as though people need more than that from their physicians. Important as skill and scientific acumen may be—and they are of the essence—something else is needed; something apparently that the "old family doctor" must have possessed, for his gradual disappearance is still talked about and regarded with nostalgia and real regret.

What was his secret and why the nostalgia? Evidently people loved him; they only rarely paid him and he was indeed a "Dutch uncle," but what quality did he possess which now is thought to be necessary? We think we know. Bálint, a British psychiatrist, says his secret was that he gave of himself: "The doctor himself is an extremely powerful drug and those who use it relieve more suffering than has yet been recorded by the most powerful drug in the pharmacopoeia. The family doctor knew this to be so and he prescribed himself in generous doses." [3] This was his secret, and this apparently is the secret of success of any professional man who must deal with people, whether they be patients, parishioners, or conferees.

As to the old doctor's legendary agnosticism, that is overrated. Most of the older physicians were taught in an era when mechanistic theories were in vogue. Symptoms always had to be due to some tangible agent. Unless he could see it, hear it, palpate it, or cut it out, the old-time doctor did not believe in it. All of that has changed. It is now recognized that one cannot treat man's physical being in isolation, and that his psyche and emotions are not simply impedimenta put there for the purpose of complicating the doctor's diagnostic efforts. Now it is incumbent upon the doctor to take heed and to enter into meaningful dialogue concerning the dignity of man, the value of human life, and the goals of

[3] Michael Bálint, "Introduction to *The Doctor, His Patient and the Illness*," *Lancet*, 1:683-688 (April 12, 1955).

man's existence—questions left unasked in the medicine of but a few generations ago.

The Hospital Movement

This is not the place to recount to you the history of the hospital movement, even though it is one of the most absorbing studies in the annals of civilization. Born of elemental human needs, the hospital has not only been a tool of society, but also its mirror, faithfully reflecting the religious, philosophic, and cultural preoccupations of the time, together with the contemporary level of medical knowledge.

The germ of the hospital idea existed even in Babylonian times. The Egyptians, Greeks, and Romans had their temples of healing, yet the whole spirit of antiquity toward sickness and misfortune was one of expediency rather than one of compassion. Charity and pity were dispensed by individuals, and then only sporadically and when the spirit moved them. It was concomitant with the spread of Christianity that the practice of ministering to human suffering on an extended scale became a guiding principle of society. It, along with preaching and teaching, was seen as part of Christ's mission. Believers very early established the rule that each community should assume the responsibility of looking after the sick, the orphans, the widowed, and the infirm. Thus the healing ministry was considered an integral part of their work, and an obligation. Today the charge to heal the sick, it is said, has been accepted by modern religious individuals with more consistent success than any other challenge to Christian directive.

The inception of the modern hospital was under Innocent III; and in the only bit of propaganda I shall disseminate today, I recount to you that he specifically required that provision be made for the mentally ill in all these institutions. Virchow traced the origins of the German city hospitals back to this same source, and it is known that practically all the historic British hospitals were related to that period. Later on, however, this heritage was forgotten, superstition spread widely, and strange concepts of mental disease prevailed. In fact, strange concepts of medical practice arose. The whole field of mental disease became separated from medical practice, and hospitals lost sight of their original mission.

Early Christian medicine showed real progress. Though none of its texts has come down to us, indications are that Christian physicians accepted Greek pathology, while rejecting the excessive Hellenic naturalism associated with it. Early Christians also inaugurated regular medical, nursing, and social assistance through their hospitals. Had Christianity been able to continue to nurture it, the history of Western medicine in general might have been different. As it was, the decline in medical practices followed upon the general decline of civilization in Europe.

It really is only in the past half century that the image of the hospital began changing from a final stopping place to a place of healing. The grandparents of some of us here had doubts about hospitals. Sir Thomas Browne despised them in his day and held them "but a place to die in." Now that fear of the hospital is gone, fear that was rooted in historic memory of scenes of tragedy.

Today the modern hospital is a place to which people may look with hope and confidence. It has taken its place beside all other institutions erected for the service of the community,

beside the churches, where the spiritual necessities of the citizens are guided; beside the schools and universities, where ancient wisdom and present-day advanced knowledge are presented to the student; beside the libraries, which house the thoughts of men long dead and of the sum total of learning and which afford residents a privileged opportunity to scan the offices and factories and commercial enterprises, which support the community and furnish an outlet for creative ingenuity of its inhabitants.[4]

In fact, the need for good hospitals and the need for attention to the physical and mental health of its citizens is an essential concern of the community. Here is an ideal starting place for continuing meaningful dialogue between theologian and medical practitioner. Man, who straddles two worlds, the present and the next, at some time in his life needs the ministrations of both disciplines.

It is not necessary for us to dwell upon the fact that, along with everything else, the hospital, as well as the medicine practiced in it, has changed markedly in the past several decades, and that these changes have influenced and have been influenced by the social scene. The infectious diseases are under control. The great scourges which formerly decimated populations have been dealt with. Childhood diseases, pneumonia, formerly known as the "captain of the men of death,"

[4] Paul V. Harrington, "The Catholic Hospital," *Hospital Progress,* 42 (June, 1961).

and tuberculosis, all have had inroads made upon them. In their places the physician now sees chronic diseases, some of them crippling, some of them fatal; emotional disorders in profusion and under various guises; and the disheartening illnesses of the older age groups.

New Challenges to Medicine and Theology

New and unforeseen medical problems emerged from modern technology and twentieth-century life. Thus hypervitaminosis has become a common form of nutritional disease in the Western world. Cigarettes and X rays have caused the increase of certain types of cancer. Detergents and various synthetics increase the incidence of allergies. And who needs to be told how often our new and powerful drugs create a worse distress than that they were meant to relieve? Well, we can go further and prophesy that the present patterns of disease also will change in the future and new conditions will arise to challenge us. With every new scientific advance accompanying hazards are bound to arise, and we must be prepared to meet them.

The phenomenon of change, therefore, is something to keep in mind. As Carlyle once observed: "Today is not yesterday. We ourselves change. How can our work and thoughts, if they are always to be fittest, continue always the same? Change indeed is painful, yet ever needful." In *Conversation at Midnight,* Edna St. Vincent Millay points out how all creatures must adapt to changing conditions under which they live:

> If they can grow new faculties to meet the necessity,
> They thrive, otherwise not; the inflexible organism,
> However much alive today, is tomorrow extinct.

Not everyone is happy about change, however, nor is everyone convinced that it is at all necessary. There are people, religious and irreligious, who are hopelessly enamored of the status quo, attached to the past and profoundly distrustful of present and future. They are said to desire nothing more passionately than to turn back the clock. These men, one clergyman noted, are sincere; they are determined; they are dangerous. They cling to a certain familiar social order, and whatever disturbs this order appears to them as an attack upon a sacred institution. These folks remind me of Aunt Sarah in *Wickford Point.* She, you will remember, developed an ingrown preoccupation with affairs that were not contemporary and an increasing predilection not to look at the present. Living in the past, someone recently observed, has only one thing to recommend it: it is cheaper.

Thus, we have the slowly dawning recognition of the necessity for closer relations between medicine and theology. We have the background of the Christian healing mission and the hospitals with their origin deeply rooted in Christian history. Added to this we are in what Teilhard called "the greatest period of change ever known." "Something is happening," he said, "to the whole structure of human consciousness. A fresh kind of life is starting. In the face of such an upheaval and actually shaken by it, no one can remain indifferent." [5]

It is certain that neither religion nor medicine can afford to remain indifferent, nor do we here imply that they have been. There have been numerous efforts to find a *via media*

[5] Pierre Teilhard de Chardin, *The Phenomenon of Man* (New York: Harper & Row, 1961).

upon which to meet to help alleviate man's distress, and these will have to continue and increase in number. At the moment it appears as though the fields of psychiatry and psychosomatic medicine offer the most likely locus for collaboration, for they deal with man's emotions and man under stress in this period of rapid change.

Unfortunately, it is in the area of change and stress that the drama of emotional upset is frequently played. The young are under stress and pressures in their academic and social lives. The middle-aged are frequently prevented from adapting to new situations and conditions due to rigidity and lack of malleability. The older age groups not infrequently are depressed because of the "lost cap of office," and because the culture seems to have no place or time for them. Here are fertile fields for collaboration, for though presenting symptoms are frequently physical, the underlying factors are often enough spiritual.

In the young people problems often appear in the guise of unrest, apathy, failure in school, rebellion against authority, and at times use of alcohol or drugs. The so-called "identity crises" are frequently marked with and heralded by the oft-repeated questions: Who am I? What do I want? Where am I going? What is the use of it all? These are wonderful young people for the most part—bright, forthright, idealistic. Today's young men have so many possibilities and so many choices before them that they often become confused and apathetic. They are in need of help and often do not know to whom to turn; hence they lean upon and emulate one another. In their efforts to avoid any evidences of conformity to rules, they end up at times conforming to the actions of the less stable of their peers.

Young people are having serious troubles about the so-called new morality—premarital sex relations; the usefulness or uselessness of beliefs they learned at home and in churches. Self-fulfillment is the cry they hear. Its basis is in situation ethics: You can do anything you want to do as long as you need it for your own self-fulfillment. This is in contrast to Christian personalism, which is not self-centered. Its fulfillment is in love and faith and concern for the community. It does not use others; it is humility, kindness to others, and openness to the world—a commitment to mankind.

I draw no invidious conclusions, but I note the great increase in young people in mental hospitals, most of them with personality or character disorders. I have no time to discuss here the results of liberalized dormitory rules in colleges. They are upsetting to some of the girls, as Dr. Graham Blaine, chief of psychiatry in the Harvard Health Service, testifies: "In coeducational colleges that have given their students free access to bedrooms, the students themselves have asked that restrictions be imposed. They have sensed a pressure to engage in a type of activity which they felt inappropriate to them." [6] Dr. Holleck, a University of Wisconsin psychiatrist, recently declared that a more lenient attitude on campus about premarital sex experience has imposed stresses on some college women severe enough to cause emotional breakdown.[7]

Dr. Blaine noted also that various fears maintained old standards for young people in the past. If these standards

[6] *Youth and the Hazards of Affluence* (New York: Harper & Row, 1966), p. 57.

[7] *Medical Tribune,* March 13, 1967.

lead to a more stable way of life for society as a whole, how can we make them more meaningful for high school and college students today? "Undoubtedly," he said, "by dealing with them on their own terms, their own language, with *quid pro quo* logic, in addition to re-enforcing the previously effective bases for those who are helped by them." [8]

Of the young people, the dean of freshmen at Harvard said: "With so many wonderful kids on the beach, it is wise to have some lifeguards handy in case they get beyond their depths." Here is an excellent opportunity for college psychiatrists and chaplains to work together. It is a fruitful mission which requires the utmost in skill, and men must be carefully prepared for it.

An equal opportunity holds for those individuals in middle life whose problems so often seem to be existential. We see at present more than the usual amount of unrest in this group, for it seems now to be a difficult transitional period. We observe emotional instability, physical complaints, boredom, an irrational fear of aging, and an urgent desire to be doing something different—all forms of calendar neurosis. This is probably the more striking now because more people live long enough to display these symptoms, in contrast to the days of our ancestors. One thinks in this regard of the Reverend Gerald Vann's comment regarding the hunger for the infinite which alone can fill the human heart, this being psychological fact and religious truth! We can envision psychology confirming belief in religious doctrine, and religion filling the needs and desires that psychology empirically reveals.

It is obvious now that the effective practice of medicine

[8] *Youth and the Hazards of Affluence,* p. 61.

cannot ignore man's emotional or spiritual problems. They are inextricably woven into his very being. They influence his actions, his life, and the symptoms he presents to the doctor. The cry for help, the quest for security, the reach for the alleviation of guilt, all have physical and emotional accompaniments. They all must be dealt with by knowledgeable people.

At present the most exciting thing happening nationally is the marked and steadily increasing interest that the community is displaying in hospitals and the entire health field. By an incredible turnabout, the community, heretofore content merely to observe, is now even willing to help with the problems of the emotionally and mentally ill. They are looking for direction and are anxious to get on with the job. Where can this effort take place? In the new comprehensive Community Mental Health Centers now abuilding. These should furnish an excellent locus for this type of community activity. The success of the venture will depend upon the interest and collaboration of public and private agencies, family doctor, clergyman, psychiatrist, psychologist, and social worker. Unless there is close collaboration, these centers will fail their purpose and become simply more clinics, expensive to run and in competition with other institutions for personnel.

Until recent widespread interest in cardiac surgery engaged public attention, the two fastest growing medical disciplines were psychiatry and rehabilitation. They advanced further in the past two decades than they had in all the years that had gone before. They came of age in World War II and they adapted to the times. Both hold promise for collaboration of medical men, rehabilitation workers, and clergymen. A great deal of wisdom and foresight and humanitarian purpose is exhibited in the statement of one of rehabilitation's most outstanding men, Dr. Howard Rusk; it breathes a direction for collaboration for the future:

> A man with a broken back has not been rehabilitated if we spend four months to teach him to walk but leave him with such an anxiety that he will not go out of the house and, if we meet this objection and then send him to a fourth floor walk-up apartment where he is a prisoner in his own room the rest of his life, we have done him no great service. Until we have found him a job which he can do, we still have not fulfilled our responsibility.[9]

The opportunities for collaboration become apparent here; it is comprehensive medicine, the care of the whole person, which is involved. I mention these two disciplines because, in addition to their hospital work, they have moved out into patients' homes. This portends the medicine of the future.

A Glance at the Future

What of the future? Fascinating advances lie before us. Heart disease certainly will be markedly lessened and inroads will be made against cancer and arthritis. Vaccines will eliminate some of the present exanthemata and cut down on the number of brain-damaged children. Aging will probably remain a mystery and man will not live too much longer than the span allotted by the psalmist. New diseases are sure to arise as we conquer the old. New drugs will appear; one to cut down cholesterol is already in the offing.

[9] Howard Rusk, "Rehabilitation," *Abbottempo* (publication of Abbott Laboratories), III (1963).

The most dramatic changes, however, will probably come in the replacement of worn-out or injured bodily organs. This is a ticklish problem and it may well have some theological connotations. Unfortunately, it will take underprivileged people in various parts of the world a long, long time to benefit from these marvels which seem so close to us in our country.

As a bit of a commercial, psychiatry, which has been the Cinderella of medicine, will have arrived in state. The fact that one cannot separate a man's psyche from his soma will long since have percolated, as will the fact that one cannot be ill physically without having some emotional accompaniments to the illness and vice versa. New fields and specialties will come into being. Nuclear substances will find wider usage. Research will aid in remarkable advances, and treatments now in use will be superseded. Hospital construction will have changed markedly and, in response to personnel shortages, will be automated fully and will utilize numerous labor-saving devices.

More and more people will be admitted to hospitals within the next few decades. The last figure I heard estimated four years ago was twenty-five million admissions. Now, with Medicare, Medicaid, and the "Medics" that are sure to follow, it will soar still higher. The increase will not be altogether due to increase in illness, but will also encompass many new tasks which society will impress upon hospitals. There will be, as there already is in psychiatry, greatly increased out-patient care of patients—day hospitals, night hospitals, halfway houses, continuous care units, rehabilitation units, and numerous satellite or daughter units, which will take some of the pressure off the emergency and acute segments of the hospital.

Moral problems to be faced by the theologians will arise at every step of the way. A number of them are already upon us. When is it morally justifiable to use a person for experimental purposes? Someone will always have to be the first one upon whom a new medical technique is tried or who will be given a new drug. The Nuremberg Code is protective of patients, but not inclusive enough. Scientific medicine has done wonders. Physical science has performed miracles but it has also released vast destructive powers, and man, now having learned to destroy this earthly planet, is having a look at the moon. Scientists are also having second thoughts about the results of their handiwork. Basic answers are needed all around as to the problem of values and meaning.

Fortunately, at a recent meeting of the American Association for the Advancement of Science it became apparent that many scientists are now worried about their social responsibilities. Dr. Thomas Malone, in a discussion of possible consequences of weather modification, said: "If it adds one more small brick to the edifice that contains world conflict and supports world order, science will have served a noble purpose by enriching human life. The burden of responsibility for seeing that this happens is, I believe, upon the scientists." [10] The wonderful thing is that he warned: "The point is that there is still time for reflective thought for setting objectives, for weighing alternative courses of action; in short, to act responsibly." [11] Meanwhile, in its ex-

[10] Thomas Malone, "The Moral Sense of the Scientists," *The Washington Post,* January 3, 1967.
[11] *Ibid.*

perimental endeavors medicine is guided by the simple pronouncements of Claude Bernard: "Among the experiments that may be tried on man, those that can only harm are forbidden, those that are innocent are permissible, and those that may do good are obligatory." [12] These will carry patients safely and will recognize their proper value and dignity until something more comprehensive is worked out.

Just two observations in closing, both of which concern physicians and theologians. The questions of family planning, population control, the easement of abortion laws, all are agitating the public, the legislators, and the news media, and all have both religious and medical connotations. A great deal of soul-searching has to be done by both groups as to what is physiological and what is moral. Dr. Albert Outler pointed up the beginning of the solution to one of medicine's problems when he said that if medicine would seek to pinpoint the precise time of ovulation, instead of working on anovulation, this would allow for "conception consciously intended instead of consciously intended *contra*ception." [13] A great deal of wisdom is encompassed in that statement. To determine exactly the time of ovulation, the time a fetus is viable, the time of death, all have medical, theological, and legal import.

Another problem in the public eye, which concerns both medicine and theology, is that of LSD and related psychedelic substances. Although admittedly the final answers have not been written and much more carefully controlled experi-

[12] Claude Bernard, *Experimental Medicine* (New York: The Macmillan Company, 1927), p. 102.

[13] Albert C. Outler, *Methodist Observer at Vatican II* (Westminster, Maryland: The Newman Press, 1967), p. 182.

mentation upon the subject is needed, in the opinion of a majority of medical men this is a dangerous drug, and its distribution should be controlled. Sufficient documentation and a large number of mental hospital admissions, plus a number of tragedies directly connected with its usage, testify to this fact.

Some individuals have written and preached about the religious or mystical experiences that may accrue from usage of the drug. Several of these men seem to be in responsible positions, and it is a serious matter for them to broadcast their opinions to groups which are just waiting for some authority to justify their experimentation and search for "a mystical experience." One writer, a professor of spiritual theology, after careful examination of the problem, says:

> As for the psychedelic drug, obviously from all that has been said it cannot produce a supernatural mystical experience. This is a gift of God. . . . The devout Christian has no need of the LSD experience in his journey to union with God and should reject it.[14]

I take it that neither physicians nor theologians really needed to be told this, but it does help to get substantiating opinions. To believe that mystical experience and the sight of God may be had by ingesting a toxic substance strains the credulity of any religious person. God is neither a pharmacologist nor a small-volt engineer. From practical experience the psychiatrist knows that the phenomena described are hallucinations and the experience is a part of an acute, short-lived toxic psychosis.

[14] Kiernan Kavanaugh, O.C.D., "LSD and Religious Experience, a Theologian's Viewpoint," *Spiritual Life*, Spring, 1967.

The question will be asked: How do we get the cooperation of the medical party in our efforts at dialogue? The physician often does not seem interested. The psychiatrist has had long experience with this type of reaction. He could not interest his medical conferees either, but he kept right at it, and today psychiatry, the stone which the medical builders once rejected, is about to become the cornerstone of the comprehensive medicine of the future. The first approach to the uninterested or inimical is to allay their anxiety. If one assumes the attitude of carrying light to the heathen, all is lost at the start.

As to relations between medicine and religion, they are like those of science and religion. One has to be careful and make sure the quarrel is not really one between adherents of both disciplines who do not understand one another. Zilboorg pointed to a conflict between what man wants to do with science and what he wants to do with religion. He said: "Make either of them purely utilitarian, power seeking, or an instrument for man's self-assertion and acting in his own behalf, and the conflict becomes not only inevitable, but intolerant and intolerable."

The collaboration of physician and clergyman should not be too difficult a task. Both disciplines know that the greatest hope for maintaining equilibrium in the face of any calamity lies within ourselves. Persons with a transcendental system of values and a deep sense of moral duty are the possessors of values which no man and no catastrophe can take from them. Under all circumstances they can maintain their peace of mind, their conviction of human dignity, their self-respect, and their sense of duty. We will have difficulties and perhaps conflict on occasion, but the stakes are high, for as Daniel Webster said:

> If we work upon marble, it will perish. If we work upon brass, time will efface it. If we rear temples, they will crumble to dust. But if we work upon men's immortal minds, if we imbue them with high principles, with the just fear of God and the love of their fellow men, we engrave on those tablets something which no time can efface, and which will brighten and brighten to all eternity.[15]

As to our attitudes toward one another while we are undertaking this task, Ruskin gave us a suggestion. He believed that the test of a truly great person is humility. He did not mean by humility doubt of one's own ability. But really great men have a curious feeling that greatness is not in them but through them, and they see something divine in every other man and are endlessly, foolishly, and incredibly merciful. This is the attitude with which we must approach one another in our efforts at collaboration.

J. Robert Nelson

The relation of theology to medicine is more than simply the relationship of the pastor or theologian to the physician. That is, we easily think of this matter as merely the intersecting of professional interests and techniques.

This is manifestly wrong. The actual relation is one between the whole Christian community, the church, and the whole complex field of human pathology and therapy. The

[15] Daniel Webster, Speech given at Faneuil Hall, Boston, 1852.

whole church, expressed in each congregation, includes the theologian or pastor as one of its members. Likewise, it includes as members a great many doctors of the medical profession and its numerous allied fields. Therefore, the Christian physician is on the side of the theologian and of every fellow member of the church, insofar as he endeavors to understand the interrelation of faith and health. The physician, surgeon, researchist, pastor, chaplain, theologian—they all meet as members of the church and confessors of faith in God through Christ. But they possess different gifts (the *charismata* of the Holy Spirit) as well as different training and responsibility. And in a very general sense, they all have the same purpose in their life's vocation: the healing, reconciling, and redeeming of human beings.

Since one of the accurate designations of a Christian is that of "forgiven sinner," we can all readily acknowledge our imperfections. Before God and one another the guard is lowered, the pretense is abandoned. The minister or theologian is not that devout and immaculate saint which social convention decrees he should be. Nor is the physician that omniscient, proficient worker of medical miracles seen in the daytime television serials. Each is to some degree the victim of the evil he opposes, whether it be superstition, sin, or sickness. Just as the pastor is an imperfect medium for the preaching and teaching of the gospel, so the physician is seldom the fully healthy person. Thus, the late poet T. S. Eliot included us all in his lines from *East Coker:*

> The wounded surgeon plies the steel
> That questions the distempered part;
> Beneath the bleeding hands we feel

> The sharp compassion of the healer's art
> Resolving the enigma of the fever chart.
>
> Our only health is the disease
> If we obey the dying nurse
> Whose constant care is not to please
> But to remind of our, and Adam's curse,
> And that, to be restored, our sickness
>   must grow worse.

In respect to faith and health and all aspects of living, therefore, we recognize and reflect upon our finitude and mortality. We are dying men talking to dying men about what it means to be alive.

Human Existence a Paradox

In one valid sense our life both as individuals and as a human race is a continuing struggle against the world, which seeks our destruction. It is true for all persons that, prior to the natural ending of life on account of age and worn-out tissues, we must struggle against the world's formidable arsenal of disease, disaster, and death. Thanks to a complex of factors we in America, as in parts of Europe, have been gaining the upper hand in this battle. The factors are medical research and practice, public health programs, economic development, and extending education. So our life expectancy has risen in just seventy-five years from little better than thirty years to the present seventy years.

In America many of us have virtually forgotten what infant mortality means; but too many Americans are ignorant or negligent of the fact that the current rate of infant mortality in Vietnam and the Congo, for example, is still fifty percent and doubtless as high in other parts of Africa, Asia, and South America. While in America we enjoy an environment in which such lethal diseases as cholera, smallpox, typhoid, tuberculosis as well as acute malnutrition have been virtually stamped out, it should be on our conscience that the great majority of human beings are still exposed and vulnerable to these killers. And in our own country we have as yet failed to overcome the dreaded heart disease and cancer. Still worse—and here we depart from consideration of diseases—there is a combination of natural and humanly caused forces which accounts for the majority of deaths of Americans under the age of thirty. These are all forms of accidents, which may occur at any minute in one's life, as well as the grim acts of homicide and suicide. And when in addition to all these elements in the picture of morbidity and mortality we add the staggering facts about mental illness in our land, it becomes amazing to us that there can be much chance for "life, liberty, and the pursuit of happiness."

It is not the business of Christian theology merely to brood upon these melancholy data of the human struggle against illness and death. But it *is* the business of theology to reflect upon the marvel of human life as God's creation, and to regard the menaces which attack life as evils within the created realm which, by divine power and human effort, can be restrained, neutralized, and even eliminated. And it is, further, the constant responsibility of Christian thinkers to remind society who a man is and what human life means.

All men apart from faith can recognize the inherent paradox of a man's existence. In relation to natural environment he is one of the hardiest and one of the most fragile and vulnerable of creatures. This marvelous human body can survive dreadful abuses, hunger, freezing, fracture, and painful buffeting. Or, on the contrary, a man can die from choking on a dry morsel of food, from a slight overdose of drugs, or from a tiny bubble or embolism in the bloodstream. All men likewise can be aware of man's apparent insignificance in the world and the universe. You and I are just a few individuals among three billion who now live and the billions who have lived heretofore. Like tiny, intelligent plankton we know ourselves to be swimming momentarily in the vastness of the seven seas.

Christian faith is not an idealistic religion. Its image of man is not that of the impersonal Greek statue; neither is it the disembodied soul or the discarnate spirit of Hinduism or theosophy. Following the insights of the Old Testament, Christians have never rightly ignored man's littleness nor minimized his greatness. In Christian anthropology there is no shying away from the imperfection and sin of the human person. The selfishness, pride, lust, and hostility which lurk in the heart of each man are not illusions. They belong to the same category as man's mortality. They are the marks of disintegration, which, along with physical disease and impairment, inexplicably detract from the true and authentic life which all people wish to enjoy. But even as men and women yearn for health and happiness, their frustrated yearnings may lead often to self-destruction or the destruction of others. This is the human paradox, *la misère et la grandeur de l'homme* (Pascal), which in the Christian perspective is unblinkingly recognized.

In the Christian view of man the earthly, bodily, fleshly existence of a person is neither an illusion nor is it merely a physical and biological matter. Because the wholeness of a person is seen in the unity of his body and his undefinable soul or ego, it is not an option but a mandate for Christians to do all things possible for the well-being of the whole person. This is a worthy goal of the church as well. Indeed, it is fundamental to the churches' well-established support of medicine and hospitals.

Men Live for Meaning

Of still greater importance than the healthy body and mind, however, is the Christian promise that human existence is, or can be, meaningful. To know that life has purpose, that one's time upon the earth is worth the struggle, trial, and pain of it all, is more important than being equipped with a body free of disease or impairment. A kind of animal vitality is fine to have, but it is not the *summum bonum* of living.

Paul Tillich was very fond of stressing the unity of health and faith. We can readily understand his identifying salvation and healing, *Heil und Heiligung,* holiness and wholeness. True as it is that physical strength and metabolic regularity are inextricably related to the condition of the mind, it remains to be asserted that the conception of meaning in life transcends both these dimensions.

Now, meaning in this mortal life implies a purpose and therefore a direction and style of living. Christian faith certainly has no monopoly on life's quality of meaning. It would be arrogant of us to claim this. But what Christian faith has is a concept of meaning which is distinctive and is, I believe, superior to all others. Without knowing or believing in Jesus Christ, one can obviously have a useful and enjoyable life. He can excel in music, athletic prowess, commerce, government, teaching, science, farming, skilled labor, and all the rest. Countless paths of achievement lie open to him in our free and prosperous society. But achievement in life's work is not the same as meaningful living. The lives of many persons testify to this lack.

When, for example, the famous writer Somerset Maugham died not long ago, it was recalled that some of his last words were filled with a personal pessimism. He had lived fourscore years in good health, had achieved a notable reputation for writing, and had become exceedingly rich. But near the end of his life he admitted that he could not in retrospect find evidence of genuine purpose in his long life. And in melancholy mood he remarked that he would not care to live this earthly life again.

What this illustrates is just that in one man's case the value of health and success was insufficient to satisfy the need for meaning.

The disclosure of meaning which comes through the person of Jesus Christ is far different from physical health, hedonism, or the power to gratify all of one's proud longings. The meaning of life in Christian terms, put simply, is the extending of authentic love for all persons, and through the best use of one's native and acquired abilities to glorify God.

This is why we say that it is a matter of Christian discipleship and moral obligation to oppose everything which injures or destroys human life—everything, that is, except one. That exception is the injury or even destruction one must risk or suffer in self-sacrifice for the sake of love. We may dodge the personal implications of this statement much of the time. The implications mean a life full of risk and strain and self-denial. But the veracity of this insight for the Christian meaning of life is indisputable and inescapable.

Threats to Health and Meaning

The Christian concern is thus to find meaning in the whole range of a person's experience. It is no more confined to concern for his physical and mental health than to his so-called religious experience. When we think of healing and health, therefore, we have to comprehend the wide complex of factors which, positively, build up and support human well-being and meaning as well as those which, negatively, work for man's destruction. Those two categories are boundless, of course. No one person can take the measure of them. But while the Christian physician or nurse or pastor or teacher does his specialized work, he can keep in mind the place of his efforts in the broad scope of the edifying and destroying forces of human life.

To be specific, consider that perennial and contemporary destroyer of goods, values, and human life; I mean, war.

Here is a paradox in the field of medical care. We know that great advances have been made in medical research because of our country's mobilization of resources for modern warfare. The army and navy continue to facilitate research and practice in medicine, surgery, psychiatry, and related fields. The Walter Reed and Bethesda hospitals are the most famous of military medical centers. And yet, for all its health-sustaining features, military medicine is inevitably integral to the huge war machine, which is designed primarily to kill the chosen enemy, and which transports thousands of American men to their untimely death.

The Montreal Expo '67 sponsored a competition of sixty-second cartoons. They were required in that short space of time to convey a significant message. An entry from Czechoslovakia was declared the winner. It showed a patient on the operating table, surrounded by busy surgeons and nurses. The operation ended, the patient arose, dressed himself in military uniform, saluted the surgeons with a grateful smile, and marched off the screen—from whence came the sound of the rifle shot which killed him. This cartoon illustrates not only the bittersweet pathos of warfare. It drives home the easily neglected truth that modern warfare cancels out its own promotion of health and scientific progress in domestic human affairs.

We should admire and support the humanitarian efforts of some American doctors to bring a few of the million maimed and burned children of Vietnam to this country for proper treatment. But we cannot avoid the bitter realization that this noble and therapeutic program is nevertheless a mere palliative applied to the gross and epidemic disease of human corruption which erupts in the form of warfare.

Perhaps the issue should be put this way: the chief contribution of the Christian faith, or the church, toward healing is the insight and motivation needed to show people that the meaningful life of love or human concern requires constant struggle to remove the causes of human misery and premature death.

The familiar adage that prevention of disease has sixteen times the value of cure may be self-evident and almost banal. But as Christian persons, groups, and churches involved in human society we have scarcely begun to act according to this manifest truth.

For example, the deploying of our resources for the maintaining of international order and peace is more than a matter of political responsibility. It is an effective aid to the health of millions who are afflicted, injured, or killed in war.

The support of public health programs, sanitation, birth control, drug control, and the like, even though they are usually carried on by public agencies, is the concern of the people who care for others. The same can be said for correction of alcoholism and even for safe driving, in view of the clear fact that the combination of alcohol and gasoline accounts for frightful loss of limb and life.

Even the opposing problems of too much or too little food must be the object of concern. Too much food causes obesity (which might be called "fat accompli") and can be deadly. Too little food, critical malnutrition from which millions are suffering this moment, is even more lethal.

As we learn more of the influence upon organic health of a person's social environment, we can better recognize the need for constant effort for the amelioration of living conditions for the rejected, the dispossessed, the poverty-stricken, and the exploited. If I understand correctly, physicians today are increasingly aware of the deleterious effects upon a child's physical health of parental rejection or hostility, of the divorce of parents, of the acids of racial discrimination and segregation. The sense of pointlessness and meaninglessness which an adolescent feels can cause not only failure in school and incipient crime, but mental or physical illness, and in extremity suicide.

In the face of these dreadful data, it must be said again that you do not have to be a Christian, or even a religious person, to know the complex and malignant causes of morbidity. But it is by no means unimportant to stress the social effect of that hypersensitivity to human misery which is the truly Christian attitude. I believe that a society or nation in which a good proportion of the people are constantly influenced by the figure of Jesus Christ as the incarnation of God's self-giving love is one which has the optimum likelihood of securing healthful conditions of living.

Four news items in one week's Boston papers illustrate the promise and the problems of the interrelation of health, healing, human concern, and social environment:

Dr. Benjamin Spock (who spent four years at Mayo Clinic) is insisting that there must be a concerted attack upon what he seriously calls the "virus of prejudice" in our society. "Prejudice is a disease that may never fully disappear," he said, "but the most crippling effects are curable."

Dr. Erich Lindemann is urging psychiatrists to provide for free or very low-cost psychiatric service to the poor people of the cities who need it desperately.

Richard Cardinal Cushing and Bishop Fulton J. Sheen are addressing hundreds of Catholic hospital administrators, saying that the staff members of hospitals should go outside their walls to extend treatment to the poor in the name of Christ, and to exert most stringent efforts to hold down the staggering costs of hospitalization.

Here are four prominent men who see the urgency of coming to terms with the sociological factors in healing.

In sharp contrast to the Catholic spokesmen, however, the young and popular theologian Harvey Cox is urging the churches fully to withdraw from the medical, clinical, and hospital field. Leave all this to the welfare state, he says, and let the churches concentrate on problems of social justice. To which I respond, "A pox on Cox!" Does he fail to see the connection between the truly Christian passion for social justice and the concern for health? If the moral and humane character of Christian faith cannot promote for the care of human beings a sense of responsibility far superior to that of the state-controlled institution, there can be little value left in Christianity to commend to citizens of the secular city.

In Conclusion

Some may charge that this social emphasis represents my wandering away from the theme of this conference. However, it seems evident to me that in this commanding concern for the social responsibility of Christian people for all aspects of human well-being we highlight a dimension of the vast problems of healing and health, which is at least equal in significance to other theoretical and technical dimensions.

For example, I can only gawk in amazement at the skills of surgeons and biochemists. And I do not minimize at all the wonderful phenomenon called "spiritual healing"; that is, rapid recovery from disease without apparent benefit of M.D. I know that in my own experience I have benefited from such an inexplicable kind of recovery from a usually mortal disease. I do believe in the present reality of a divine power for the restoration of life, which was supremely operative in Jesus Christ during his brief earthly ministry.

As a Methodist, I must yet dismiss our John Wesley's experiments in medicine, or "physick," as quaint and perhaps a bit quackish. But I can still respond with a peculiar fervor to that powerful symbolism of the last stanza of the hymn written by his brother Charles, "O for a Thousand Tongues to Sing":

> Hear him, ye deaf; his praise, ye dumb,
> Your loosened tongues employ;
> Ye blind, behold your Savior come;
> And leap, ye lame, for joy.

11. The Bible Speaks to the Health of Man

Seward Hiltner

Before this discussion is completed, I trust it will be clear that there is a biblical message about health that applies to us today as well as to those of biblical times. This message as I hope to get to it is about the nature of health, about the context in which health is to be understood, about the general means by which health may be sought, and perhaps above all about the place of health in the human hierarchy of values. But I am going to begin at another point. I shall come to those matters in due course.

We cannot grasp the biblical understanding of health, however, if we approach the Bible without prior critical reflection on our own Western and modern assumptions about health. We must clean our own spectacles, or we shall, however unwittingly, cloud and distort what the Bible says about this.

I shall, therefore, begin with an attempt to state the main assumptions made by men of modern Western culture, including Christians, about health. Then, with these assumptions in perspective, I shall try to state what the Bible does and does not say about health. I shall then consider the implications of the biblical message for the kind, degree, and scope of our current attentiveness to health. And my conclusion will try to give some kind of modern definition of health that attempts to put health in its proper place, according to the implications of the biblical message and modern knowledge.

Modern Assumptions About Health

We Westerners assume—and do not bother to argue—that health represents some kind of capacity in the individual person. Its assumed focus is the individual person.

Of course we acknowledge such realities as public health or even social health. We purify our water supplies, pasteurize our milk, inoculate against smallpox and polio. We have even begun to make some moves toward "community mental health" and not just the mental health of individual persons. But always we assume that the focus of our efforts is, finally, the individual.

This slant toward individualism is not reprehensible. It may be, and often is, our Western way of being attentive to the needs of the "least of these," and in that sense it is obedient to our Lord's injunction. But this individualistic slant about health is not found in the Bible. If, therefore, we approach the Bible without recognition of our slant, we shall fail to hear what it says. Whatever its merits, our modern individualistic slant must be acknowledged as such before we can approach the Bible with an open mind.

Second, we Westerners assume that there can be no more than a metaphorical or analogical relationship between health, understood as focused in the individual person, and the working out of God's purposes for mankind. We do, today, acknowledge the analogy. We admit that society is broken, disrupted, disintegrated; that it, too, along with the individual person, needs the healing that leads to health. But none of us really believes that God looks upon this gigantic task of cosmic healing in the same way as upon our individual virus infections, toothaches, arterioscleroses, and neuroses. We make an analogical and metaphorical connection, but we are wary of an identity. Is all health derivative from "cosmic health"? That is not a modern Western question. We certainly hope that God, despite human sin, will manage to pull off some kind of cosmic health and healing. But what we can see, feel, and touch is our own health. Are we alive? Can we walk, talk, smell, worship, go to parties, and visit the bank? If we can, then we are, at least relatively, healthy. God's concern for the total cosmic rivenness is important, but it is only analogous to health.

For the most part, the biblical treatment of health cannot understand our modern Western slant. In a penetrating article on the relation of religion and health, Paul Tillich emphasized the distinction.[1]

A symptom of the cosmic disorder is the enmity between the different parts of nature and between man and nature. The order of nature, called "covenant" between God and "the beasts of the field" (Hos. 2:18) is broken, and the result is chaos and self-destruction. Psalm 90, in its oldest part, complains in unison with many pagan witnesses of the laborious life and early death of man, explaining it by the breach between God and man, thus echoing the old myth of paradise lost in the fall. The land itself fell sick, and produces weeds under the curse of God, which results in enmity between man and animals (represented by the serpent), extreme pain in childbirth, fratricide, and above all, in the loss of the food of the Gods (the fruits of the tree of life) which in paradise continually overcame the natural mortality of man.[2]

[1] "The Relation of Religion and Health: Historical Considerations and Theoretical Questions," *Review of Religion* (May, 1946), pp. 348-84.

[2] *Ibid.*, pp. 349-50.

In the early biblical view, Tillich rightly asserts, the locus of sickness was cosmic. The problem was not how, beginning with individual toothaches and viruses, you make cosmic analogies, but it was, rather, understanding individual ills derivatively from the cosmic sickness. As Tillich also correctly notes, the Bible, even in its cruder early portions, rejects a "calculating moralism" that would try to trace specific sicknesses to specific acts.[3] By implication, the Bible also rejects the moralism of works whereby your positive health has been earned primarily by your attention to diet, exercise, psychic ventilation, and anything else within your power. The biblical focus is in participation rather than achievement.

A third modern slant about health has had more attention in recent years and is less likely than the two already noted to distort our vision in approaching the Bible. But it is tricky nevertheless. This slant lies in the conviction that, although we should try to get the somatic and the psychic back together, we do not see their being sundered as anything more than an unfortunate historical accident. We may even have moral fervor about the merger. We regard this as an object for achievement and not as an occasion for repentance.

So long as the health of the person was seen as derivative from cosmic health and healing the "psychic realm" was, as Tillich notes, decisive.[4] With no negation of the reality of the body, one did not move from alleged reality of body to inferential and adduced (maybe) reality of psyche, as the modern position tends to do. When this modern direction of thought became fixed, Tillich notes, salvation became con-

[3] *Ibid.*, p. 350.
[4] *Ibid.*

cerned with the individual soul, and healing became preoccupied with the individual body.

I am not recommending a return to some kind of primal unity that would ignore the enormously beneficent results of our modern, differentiated knowledge about conditions both psychic and somatic. Nevertheless, whatever the merits of our modern knowledge, we cannot understand the biblical view unless we note our current slant and make allowance for it.

Fourth, our modern assumptions about health tend to escalate it on a scale of values so that, finally, the seeking of true health tends to be at the very top of the hierarchy of values. No matter whether you are having surgery, psychoanalysis, exercise, group confrontation, yogurt, hobbies, or a sense of humor—they are all justified because they make you healthy. Show the free functioning of your limbs, or your complexes; boast of the energy investment in your guitar or your band saw; demonstrate that you can say no, when necessary, without getting all worked up over it; put your blood count through the laboratory and get a clean bill; and above all, show you can get some humorous perspective on your own foibles when threatened. I honestly believe all these to be desirable adaptive characteristics if human beings can latch on to them. But is it not a "slant" that their being built into the human character has to be "justified by health"? Is health not, thereby, made not only into a kind of "works," but also into the value that goes without questioning? Is health really that determinative of human existence? If we have true health, can all else be derivative or unimportant? Right or wrong, this is the modern Western slant.

Fifth and finally, it is our modern assumption that salvation is "religious" and health is either "secular" or at least "ecumenical" or "catholic." We assume that everybody is interested in "health," but only those who share our slant are interested in "religion" or "salvation." As apologetic strategy, perhaps there is much to be said in favor of this assumption. But it seems entirely innocent of the fact that, as William Temple once put it, God is interested in a great many things besides religion.

As Tillich said in the first sentence of the article I have been quoting, "The word 'religion' is not a religious word." [5]

Men engaged in exercising what religion designates as significant are attempting in obedience (i.e., hearing God's Word) to bring appropriate action in the world through reconciliation of division and reunion of the divided, all within the limits of actual human ambiguity and conflict. To them, religion is not a separated area but the source and motivation for all their efforts.

Another way to put the modern assumption is that you may "take" religion or "leave" it. This is biblically unthinkable. You may defy God, evade him, miss the mark in your relation to him. But the real issue is what you do in relation to his will and his intent—not whether you take or leave something separated, called "religion."

With this assumption in full operation, one of two kinds of things tends to follow. Either one assumes that, because health is "secular" rather than "religious," God has no particular interest in it. Or else, one extrapolates from the relationship between words for "health" and those for "salvation" and concludes that all the positive virtues God wants

[5] *Ibid.*, p. 348.

are subsumed under the rubric of "health." In the latter view, health becomes an imperialism. If you have this, in the true sense, all other values are corollary and derivative. In the former view, you seek health and salvation in utterly different ways. But, in either view, there is a very perceptible slant. The Bible would understand neither view.

What the Bible Does and Does Not Say About Health

As the previous discussion has implied, the Bible considers health as an individual possession only derivatively from social or cosmic health; refuses to consider the alleged free functioning of the person, psychically or physiologically, apart from what purposes he is functioning for; makes no basic distinctions between the psychic and somatic in dealing with health; does not make something like "health" in the modern definition the *summum bonum* of human life; and refuses to separate "health" from "religion," since it does not know any "religion" that is a mere optional decision in life.

It is of the greatest significance that Paul, Christian as he became, opted for his Jewish heritage in understanding things like health, instead of being beguiled by his Graeco-Roman environment. As his letter to the Romans shows, with underscoring in the Corinthian and Galatian letters, Paul retained Jewish holism about God's creation. Man was a body (soma) and psyche whose potentiality as spirit was derivative from God's own character as Spirit. Man's unity was spiritual, in no possible kind of contradiction to his bodily and psychic reality, but in dependence upon God and "in his image," with appropriate finite limitations noted.

The essence of man is his spiritually derivative unity from God himself. Functionally speaking, man is an animated body, not an intangible animation that happens, for temporal life, to inhabit a body. Body, mind, and spirit—as if all items were on the same categorical level—is not a Christian conception. Man is body. Body includes psyche. Spirit is both man's unity and his essential context as organic creature but made in the image of God, and properly attentive to God. Spirit is not in the categorical line of soma and psyche. It answers a different question.

The second thing the Bible says about health is that, whatever it is, you cannot have it alone. Health is collective and social. Do not be beguiled by freedom from specific afflictions. And do not regard the presence of a formidable thorn in the flesh as a necessary impediment to your appropriate life vocation; get on with the business of obedient response to God's vocation, thorn or not. Here is no derogation of basic ability to function, somatically and psychically; but, at the same time, no perfectionism about the "ease" of functioning. Thorn in the flesh or no, get on with living, witnessing, and working. Stop any tendency to wait until all conflicts are solved, all psychic tensions released, all somatic conditions taken care of—get on with hearing and heeding what God has called you, uniquely, to do. Health? Come off this perfectionism, friend. If you can walk, talk, think, reflect, and give thanks to our Lord, you have the "health" base. Quit stewing about it. Get going, and witness to his mighty acts in rescuing us human beings from what would otherwise be our fate.

The Bible implies that healing, at every level and with no particular distinction among the levels, is good from God's point of view. Function restored is God's will, whether the previously lost function be ability to walk or, as in the case of the Gadarene, ability to communicate with his fellows. God is for, with, and in all healing processes, at any level whatsoever. In the modern situation, God is equally present in the surgeon's tools, the psychiatrist's conversations, the internist's nutritional prescriptions (if accurate), and the pastor's prayer. God is for healing, in the sense that restoration of function, with necessary supporting structures, is always desirable.

The Bible is supportive of whatever processes genuinely lead in a healing direction. It is not necessarily in favor of immediate easing of pain, apart from the larger directional context. On the other hand, those nineteenth-century people who tried to stop the easing of unnecessary pain in the delivery of babies, on the ground that God had intended women to suffer in childbirth, are implicitly chastised by the much more dialectical understanding of the Bible. Pain that can be relieved should be relieved, according to the Bible, so long only as it does not pile up new problems later on. Thus, the biblical account is not against the interim suffering, for instance, of psychotherapy. For psychotherapy's context and structure assure that, whatever the interim suffering, suffering is not its ultimate goal.

The Bible says that illness and suffering and pain, no matter what the specific causes, are proper subjects of Christian concern and of the means of healing. It gives no guarantee that all suffering can be alleviated. But, when alleviation is possible, the Bible is not of two minds. No withholding of antibiotics from people with syphilis; no resort, with alcoholic sufferers, to indictments at the cost of cure; no condemnation of neurotic patients in the sense that would clear somebody's conscience but stand against their hopes for change.

In the story of the Gadarene psychotic sufferer, Jesus is reported to have asked him his name, and his reply was, "Legion," i.e., a thousand. True, there may well have been a thousand forces working within him. But the man who can recognize a thousand forces is, in some important sense, more than those forces. The Gadarene might well have replied, therefore, "There are nine hundred and ninety forces —but there is also me." Jesus, in the story, appealed to the "me." He saw and supported the integrity which, no matter how conflicted, could declare itself by its recognition of diversity.

The Bible does commend faith as an attitude and relates it on occasion to health and healing. But even though Jesus said to some, "Your faith has made you whole," a larger number of his healings was effected without reference to faith in the persons healed. Thus, faith as positive responsiveness to God's goodness and his healing power is acknowledged; but by implication this view of faith bars calculation, as if a person would set out to get faith so that he might be healed. Further, the presence of faith does not necessarily guarantee healing, and its absence does not necessarily prevent healing. Thus, although there is no one place in the New Testament where all these factors are considered systematically, it seems clear that the view of the relationship that faith bears to health and healing is complex and refutes any of the one-sided interpretations that may be based on a single text out of context.

The New Testament attitude toward the relation of sin

and sickness is similar to that toward faith and health. Although the connection between sin and sickness is not denied, in some general sense, Jesus explicitly rejected any calculated attempt to "blame" illness on specific sins. In relation to the man born blind, he said, "It was not that this man sinned, or his parents . . ." (John 9:3). To which he added, "but that the works of God might be made manifest in him," thus redirecting the attention of his questioners away from mere calculation to God's power and love and design.

As to the means whereby healing is effected and health restored, it is especially important that we not unwittingly modernize the biblical account. The most important fact about the biblical view is the absence of any indication that God prefers some kind of "religious" means of healing. Whatever the means used by Jesus in his healings—in the case of the man born blind, he used a lump of clay—such means are obviously not competitive with the specifics of modern medicine. They are symbolic; they point beyond themselves to the power of God regardless of the means used. They remind us forcibly of Tillich's statement that "religion" is not a religious word.

Put in positive fashion, this refusal of the Bible to be preferential toward "religious" means of healing may be stated as the recognition that all appropriate means of healing are from God. Thus, the unprecedented knowledge and skill of modern medicine are also from God. But our modern individualistic slant should not permit us to conclude from this point that awareness of the power of God standing behind all healing may be dispensed with. It is just here that there is gravest danger of distortion. Modern man is likely to say, "If you can show me that prayer will cure my chilblains, then I'll pray; but if prayer is not specific, then why not just trust the doctor?" It is almost impossible for modern man to think of health in other than these terms of calculation and contrivance. The Bible of course will have none of this.

We may ask finally what value the Bible assigns to health and healing. And even in asking the question, we must be wary of loading it. Since virtually all the ancient words for health, healing, and salvation are either identical or closely related, it is possible to take, as some have done, modern notions of health with their individualized and compartmentalized connotations, apply them to the Bible without noting the presuppositional differences, and conclude falsely that health, in the modern sense, is the highest value; that is, that all other virtues may be subsumed under "health." From the biblical point of view, on the other hand, that highest value lies in "wholeness," but in a wholeness that means relatedness to God and to one's fellow man, even the kind of cosmic wholeness to which Tillich points. This is by no means necessarily the same thing as individual health in the modern sense.

I do not believe for a minute that we modern men can dispense with the modern conception of health. And insofar as this conception is properly expanding to include mental health, we must be still more for it. But we ought not to confuse this necessary conception with the center of the biblical concern in such fashion as wrongly to conclude that if you have health everything else will be added unto you. The correct inference from the Bible is, I believe, that health in the modern sense is something necessary as a base upon which other values are built. But the presence of health does not in itself guarantee those values, nor does it replace them.

The Bible and Attention to Health

From this point onward, the term "health" is used without apology in the modern sense as something which individual persons have or do not have in various degrees, and which is relatively independent of whether one is Christian, Moslem, Communist, or atheist. From the biblical perspective, how much attention and what kind should man pay to health in this sense?

In light of the holism that Christianity drew from its Jewish ancestry, the first point is clearly that man should devote very serious attention to health as defined. The human body is not a second-class citizen. Properly animated and related, it *is* the human being and hence deserves serious attention. And since all men and not just Christians are made in the image of God, the attention to bodily health must similarly extend to all mankind.

Provision of medical care, public health services, adequate nutrition, and similar concern for mental health—from a Christian perspective all these must be steadily advanced into the most remote corners of the earth, no matter who actually carries out the technical procedures. Nor do we need to be apologetic about a reasonable attentiveness to the guarding and restoring of health in ourselves.

A second point that may be inferred from the Bible is that the health (in the modern sense) that is best performing its function is, except at moments of threat, the most automatic in operation. The nutritional health of children is best served when they have enough to eat and the right kind of food, not when they are deprived or have to scramble for what they eat. The less attention they need to pay to nutrition, the more free they are to develop and exercise appropriate social values. Conversely, the more energy they must devote to getting food, the less they have left for other values. Something similar is true in psychic life. Except for occasions of threat, which should be responded to as such, the best mental health is that which is least compulsively preoccupied with itself. By the same token, the best exercise, recreation, nutrition, and the like are those patterns of life which are least compulsively preoccupied with health and are most welcomed for their own sake.

I have already indicated that the advantages of relatively automatic function have to be set aside when there is threat. The corresponding point, as doctors have been telling us for some time, is regular checkups, treatment in early stages, and conservative medicine that does not try desperate measures until others have failed to work. Perhaps someday we can see that early checkups, in the psychiatric and psychological areas, are as important as in general medicine. This kind of attentiveness to potential threats is clearly consistent with the biblical witness. In addition to accepting the checkup wisdom for ourselves, the biblical witness requires concern that checkup facilities be available for everybody; that no one be deprived because of race, creed, color, geography, or money. Some, like Christian Scientists, may elect to reject checkups as they reject medical treatment. But if so, it is on their own decision and not by exclusion on the part of others.

Still considering health in the modern individualistic sense, a third implication of the Bible involves the kind and degree of attentiveness to health when it is seriously threatened. It is intensely human, under these conditions, to be almost wholly preoccupied with health. I see nothing in the biblical account that would warrant feelings of guilt over such preoccupation in these circumstances. The preoccupation should properly drive us to get the best care and treatment possible; and it may well also motivate us to some other properly prudential matters like making a will. Beyond that, it ought certainly to stimulate some further reflection about life and death, whether on one's own or, in the case of Christians, aided by pastoral ministry. The age-old wisdom about courage in confronting suffering and death is no less needed in our age of medical miracles; but this wisdom has never said that God rejects him who has to work toward courage through acknowledgment of bitterness, hostility, or despair.

Finally, I think that the degree and kind of attentiveness to health, in the modern sense, are always to be understood as under God's judgment. Judgment in this sense is a discriminating appraisal, not ours. We need to be equally careful not to ignore it or to assume that we can tell infallibly what it is.

Under the perspective of God's judgment we may look, for instance, at the relative value of longevity. Let us suppose that a person in early adult years plans out his entire life with a focus on protection of his health in the modern individualistic sense: a minimum of strain, of worry, of risk, of involvement—never an exotic dish, no snow shoveling, no emotion-arousing interests, and so on. And suppose that our hypothetical health-hound lived to be a hundred. The question then would be not so much whether he *had* health for his century, but rather whether his overriding preoccupation with his health was in fact idolatry—bad not so much for what it produced, namely a hundred years, as in what it prevented. To change the metaphor, is not this kind of person a tool-sharpener, who has long ago forgotten that tools are designed for use? This hypothetical illustration suggests, I think, that the term "health" in the modern sense no doubt does apply to such a person, even if he never did anybody any good; but that, humanly, his concern for his health, which should have been *preparation* for life, became life's focus. Health, yes; God's judgment, not so good.

It would be easy to run through some other health faddists with a similar eye: those who indulge themselves in the care of every small ill; those who count legalistically on the indefatigable pursuit of certain do's or don'ts; those who pursue a kind of Asklepion rainbow by shopping from doctor to doctor in the hope of finding one who agrees entirely with them; and many others. As affluence increases and health care facilities become more expert, preoccupations of these kinds become temptations for more people. I doubt that God's judgment gives them an unqualified "yes."

But on the other hand, and perhaps especially among men in our society, there is still a kind of pseudo-virile inattentiveness to health: perhaps not seeing a doctor unless one is hauled in unconscious; perhaps neglecting whatever the doctor has ordered; more probably and often, ignoring equally one's teeth and one's complexes. Seeking assistance on problems of mental health is, especially for men, more difficult in our society than submitting one's virus or break. On this side, too, I am inclined to think God's judgment does not merely reinforce the cultural pressures.

But God's judgment as we seek health for ourselves or others is not negative about appropriate use of medical and other health facilities, about taking treatment even when it involves risks, about checkups before there is trouble or when trouble is in early stages, or about every effort we can make to extend such services to all people. I believe that God is equally with the person who, when he needs it, submits himself for surgery, and with him who, also when he needs it, plucks up his courage and applies for psychiatric treatment. Indeed, since the first can be turned over to the surgeon while the second requires continuing responsibility by the patient himself, I am inclined to think that God may be even more with the second patient than the first.

God is, I believe, when we define health in the modern sense, very much for everything that protects it, enhances it, and treats it—so long only as the human attentiveness to it is, save at the moments of threat and suffering, seen as a necessary base to the realization of all other human values, but not as the substitute for those values. Health is to enable. It is not in itself the object of the enablement.

In Conclusion

Let me conclude by returning to the place where I began, namely, to the importance of distinguishing our modern assumptions about health in the modern context from the concerns and context of the Bible. Within this summarized account, I hope I have been faithful to what the Bible does and does not say. But, since both you and I are moderns, I have not hesitated to declare that our modern conceptions of health, with all their individualism and even potential idolatry, are positive and not reprehensible, so long as we do not confuse them with the central biblical message about wholeness as the Bible understood it.

But Christians today, even though rightly paying attention to health as our own modern culture regards it, and trying to get biblical judgment upon that conception and the ways of protecting and enhancing it, cannot ignore the biblical message about the social, even cosmic, understanding of health and healing, which has no special preferences about method and no calculation about results in the individual disorder. Whether well or sick, Christians pray to the God and Father of our Lord Jesus Christ—yes, for healing too, even in the modern sense—but not as a calculated substitute for medicine, nor as a mere aid to recovery. Their prayer is unabashedly human; it is honest about how they really feel; from God there is no concealment. But the thrust is toward greater awareness of God's purpose and his grace, for becoming attuned to his cosmic work of reconciliation. For no Christian is it easy. But those to whom much grace has been given may finally pray and say, as did Paul, "If we live, we live to the Lord, and if we die, we die to the Lord; so then, whether we live or whether we die, we are the Lord's" (Romans 14:8).

DISCUSSANTS

Howard J. Clinebell, Jr.

I am sure that you will all agree that we have been fed richly by Seward Hiltner's stimulating and probing paper. He has given us a foundational statement of great value, which illuminates many of the key issues in the area of religion and healing. In his scholarly, insightful approach—and particularly his discussion of the biblical and the modern views of health—he has presented us with a basic understanding of our situation and of the need for developing new correlations of religion and healing.

Our search is for guiding images—images which will guide our efforts to develop *new* understandings of the intricate relations between religion and healing and *new* bases for interprofessional cooperation. It is at this point that it would seem to me that there is an omission in Seward Hiltner's description of the modern picture of health. Building on what he has set forth, I would like to point out that there is an increasing convergence of the biblical view of health and the working assumptions of the most forward-looking healing arts. In this area, the strange new world of the arts of healing is coming ever closer to the "strange new world of the Bible." This fact is of crucial importance to us because it means that we now have a new ideological basis for cooperation between clergymen and physicians, a new bridge for communication and collaboration. The trends in medicine which have produced this give every indication of being the wave of the future. These trends are already well established and are already like a minor hurricane of influence blowing through the social sciences and all the helping disciplines, including pastoral care and counseling. The trends are the result of a new understanding of illness based on a new understanding of man—which is very close to the biblical understanding of man.

The question of the nature of man's illnesses can be answered meaningfully only in the context of the answer to a previous question: "What is man?" As Dr. Hiltner has pointed out, an individualistic view of sickness and health dominates the modern scene. This is especially true of the man on the street. It is also true of *some* professionals. But a growing number of persons in all the helping professions have recognized the fundamental inadequacy of any individualistic view of man, and of the individualistic views of sickness and health derived therefrom. It is here that (usually without knowing it) they are moving toward the biblical view of man and of sickness and health.

The new view of the nature of man can be described in various ways—the whole-man-in-his-interpersonal-world, the bio-psycho-social view, or the organismic view. Man is not adequately understood as a being whose boundaries are his skin; rather, his being includes and is defined by the nature and quality of all his significant relationships. There is a sense in which it is more accurate to say that a man *is* his relationships than to say that he *has* relationships. As sociologist Otto Pollock puts it, man is an open system which is dependent for the very essence of his being as man on the give-and-take of relationships. He becomes a *human* being only in relationships, and he can maintain his sanity, health, and humanity only through such relationships. Sickness and health both occur within this context; both have interpersonal roots and meaning. Certainly healing of the whole man can be understood only when man is seen for what he is—the center of a network of interacting relationships.

Erik Erikson has pointed out that the strength of the individual's ego—his sense of identity as a person—always depends on the mutual guarantees of strength given and received from all those whose life cycles intertwine. In a similar vein, Nathan Ackerman has indicated that the identity of the individual is completed in the "marital pair identity" of a good marriage, that the marital pair identity is the basis of and is completed in the "family identity" as children are added to the marriage, and that the strength of the family's identity is contingent to some extent on the supportive identity of the extended family and the wider community. Sickness, health, and healing all take place within these concentric circles of the search for meaningful identity.

Let me illustrate the organismic view of man as it is influencing the healing disciplines by citing experiences in one of the healing disciplines—pastoral counseling. Recognizing that physical illness and marital health are often interrelated, the perceptive pastoral counselor will often keep in communication with the couple's physician as he helps them with their marriage pain. The clergyman should also be aware of the fact that the marital disintegration and the physical symptoms may be the effects of personality-destroying social malignancies such as discrimination and economic injustice. Here is where the pastoral and the prophetic dimensions of ministry are in reciprocal relationship with each other and with the healing skills of the physician.

Or take another illustration of the organismic approach to man and sickness. Conjoint family therapy is an increasingly widely used methodology for helping troubled children and adolescents, including those who express their inner distress and hunger in physical symptoms. At one child guidance clinic with which I am familiar, it has been shown that treating the whole family in joint interviews is often more effective as well as more efficient than the older approach on a one-to-one basis. The reason for this is that conjoint therapy gets at the source of the child's disturbance—the pained family organism, including the troubled marriage of the parents. Take the case of a mother who manipulates and controls her entire family by her illnesses. She uses her physical symptoms to line up the children against the father.

To attempt to treat her physical problems in isolation from the interpersonal relationships which give them their usefulness and meaning is to miss the root of the difficulty. Incidentally, family therapy is very relevant to the work of the well-trained pastoral counselor since the minister deals constantly with family units. It would seem to be a natural methodology for the parish minister and for the family doctor.

The fact that sickness and health are interpersonal phenomena is evident to those who work with alcoholics. Perhaps you have known the wife of an alcoholic who became extremely troubled—developed an ulcer, a heart problem, had a "nervous breakdown," or became an alcoholic herself —*after her husband recovered.* Another common example is that of the family in which the delinquent or "black sheep" adult reformed and his role was taken over by someone who had previously been a "white sheep." Apparently the deviant behavior was serving a function in the total family economy; if so, treating the family organism is the method by which the basic problem can be healed.

How does a child learn a style of sickness or health? He learns it in the family setting which, in turn, reflects the community values. How does one understand a wife's heart attack as it relates to her marriage to an alcoholic? Is it a one-way street—that is, is she sick because she is married to an alcoholic? This is only part of the picture. Only by seeing the two-way street, the give-and-take of the relationship, can the dynamic function of her heart attack and an appropriate approach to treatment be understood.

Community psychiatry—the most important and exciting development in mental health in this century—has emerged, in part, from the recognition that a person *is his relationships,* and that sickness and health are produced in and by one's total interpersonal environment. Community psychiatry is having a profound and increasing impact on our understanding of health and healing of all kinds.

This relational approach to sickness and health provides a new challenge for pastoral care. The uniqueness of the minister's contribution to healing comes into focus here. Pastoral care centers on relationships—with God, self, and others; it is particularly concerned with the haunting, cosmic loneliness of modern man. The absolutely unique dimension of the pastor's role is as an expert in spiritual growth—his ministry of meanings. The problem of "value vacuums" (Viktor Frankl) is behind many physical and psychological problems. As a spiritual growth facilitator, the minister has an indispensable contribution to make to the collaborative efforts of the healing team. His training in theology and the many disciplines to which he is exposed in seminary should equip him to help persons whose problems of unhealth are symptoms of their inner emptiness, their lack of values by which to live, their frustrated longing for relationships of trust with God and with neighbor.

Robert Nelson reminded us that the total problem of sickness and health relates to the whole Christian community. This is another way of saying what I have been saying. The path to true wholeness is always an interpersonal path. As the Bible puts it, "We are members one of another." It is my conviction that this guiding biblical image, as it is now reemerging in the healing arts, is a hope image in that it points to the resolution of the conflict between the two views of health described in Dr. Hiltner's paper. The dichotomy is already in the process of being bridged. The new images of health pick up both the strengths of the biblical view—of the corporate nature of health—and the strength of the "modern" view with its emphasis on the individual. A new, creative synthesis which respects the uniqueness and mystery of each individual, but also recognizes his place in the fabric of humanity, is in the process of emerging. It is a part of our task, as persons of religious dedication, to make our contribution to this synthesis.

Roy Nichols

Dr. Hiltner described Western civilization as individualistic and partitioned. With this, of course, we have to agree, because it is evident. When he indicated that this state is contrary to the position in the Bible on wholeness and health, I was thinking of the way in which the disease of leprosy was dealt with in the Old Testament, and the way the medicinal therapies and techniques were coupled with the office of the priest in a rather practical manner. I think I am correct in saying that historically theologians, both Roman Catholic and Protestant, have contributed to the separation that we now discuss. As a matter of fact, I am beginning to believe that a good deal of our current discussion on the subject of the sacred and the secular is setting us back, rather than advancing our steps toward unity with the other disciplines. This leads me to ask three questions:

As a pastor of a local church, let me ask: Where do we begin in the effort to recover a sense of oneness between the so-called spiritual, psychic, and physical therapies, consistent with the biblical guidelines that we have heard described?

Second, do you think the new interest in healing services aids or retards the progress toward a unified approach to health and to healing? How can its values contribute toward a closer relationship between the minister and the medicine man?

Finally, what basic revisions are required in the mentality of the modern medical man and the modern theologian and pastor, if we are not only to think together but to work together for the health and healing of our people? This relates not only to the issue of equality in our regard for each other; it includes, parenthetically, the equalizing of fees.

I had two experiences that I would like to submit in conjunction with these questions. For two years I worked as a ward attendant in a hospital. Then, some years later, as an officer in the community, I presided as chairman of a group studying a rehabilitation center that had been beautifully constructed but had entered into controversy because of some disagreement between the professionals. Looking at it from these two perspectives, I saw that medical men are just like other people. And the basic problems that we confront are essentially still in the area of ego expression, concern for a certain province which we protect and a certain position which we occupy.

As a pastor of a local church, I speak constantly to people and refer them to doctors. We attempt frequently to work with doctors, but, for the most part, there is little or no interchange. Now, I say this not critically. But if we are really serious about having the people sense the common ministry of healing of which we are speaking, then we need local bridges that are as significant as the kind of bridge that we are constructing here in a meeting among sophisticated leaders.

The people need this sense of the relatedness between the preachers and the doctors. According to the Bible, both the preachers and the medical men are off the track. How do we get back?

Response by Dr. Hiltner

Our increasing understanding from the social and biological sciences convinces us that we are dealing here with relational phenomena, network phenomena.

You see, I am not against focusing on the individual when it is the individual that needs to be focused on. I do not want family therapy in the operating theater for surgery. There are appropriate times and places for individual therapy. We should avoid any kind of nostalgic going back to the Bible. It has been said that since the Bible did not have operating theaters or offer individual medical attention neither should we. Or since the Bible knew nothing of psychiatry, it is awful for us to spend hours in psychotherapy. I think that is nonsense. Modern medical care of each patient is the kind of individualism to which we are most deeply committed.

But Dr. Clinebell notes, and I agree with him, that much more is involved. And yet, I think I would have to caution him, too, as well as myself. Let us suppose we were able, by appropriate means, and no matter who does it, doctors or clergy, to help more of these families in distress, of the kind he indicates. And that does not mean that people who are concerned about restoration of health are the best experts about families.

It seems to me a lot of families can be helped, not because their health in that sense is bad, but because they do not have the other values. So we note a danger, even in what is happening today, of having an increased doctrine of justification by health alone, without much grace behind it.

To Dr. Nichols' penetrating and difficult questions I can obviously say very little in a minute or two. Let me mainly acknowledge their relevance and significance. Where do we begin today, in practice, to achieve a sense of wholeness or integration of all these disciplines? We see it developing around us here in Rochester. Where do we get hold of this integration? The one thing I have tried to say in my discussion is: I do not think we can get there by assuming we know exactly what is to be done, so that all we have to do is find good ways of dressing it up and selling it to people. This whole area in medicine and elsewhere has suffered because we have not had enough critical analysis of what we mean by health. The actual literature, the critical literature, that tries to analyze the meaning of health from medicine or other disciplines, is very small. We have all kinds of illustrations of fine things to be done or already done. But we see very little discussion of the essential definition of health.

My paper has tried to focus at that kind of point. If we are going to get to this integration interprofessionally, whether it be in a local church or elsewhere, we cannot simply assume that we have the fundamental answer, and the only question is how to convey it. We need to do more serious rethinking of our basic premises.

Dr. Nichols asked particularly about the relation between physicians and clergymen. I thought he was especially relevant in indicating that even those of us who come to conferences like this may not do so well back in the home church. We have all kinds of barriers there and not necessarily barriers of antipathy. Often the barriers coexist with our liking each other in terms of personal friendship.

Above all we need to ask: What is the function of the clergyman as the general leader of the religious community in all these endeavors? About this we both need to be inquiring, declarative, and nonapologetic. But somehow or other I have a strong feeling it is going to be very difficult to integrate the healing team in a local church, unless we have support from the kind of effort we are engaged in here.

Raymond D. Pruitt

Those who have commented so far on Dr. Hiltner's address were clergymen. I am invited to offer a few words from the standpoint of a physician, and with your indulgence I shall proceed.

Our discussion, directed to the topic "The Bible Speaks to the Health of Man," is indeed relevant to the purposes of this convocation. It seems to me therefore significant and highly appropriate that Dr. Hiltner expressed for us the ancient biblical heritage of healing insight. I can say this with unqualified enthusiasm and admiration because I am not one of his union. I speak as a physician when I say that he has laid down a creed which carries a universality that is worthy of the contemplation of each of us.

As a clinician I found Dr. Hiltner's precepts covering endless numbers of illustrations that I had seen as clinical phenomena over the years. I have always been annoyed by the octogenarian in search of the fountain of youth. My resentment of it as a search and goal unto itself needed a little theological backing.

I understand that I must deal with this phenomenon with compassion, even as I must attempt to deal with all other absurdities of human performance with compassion.

I have, on the other hand, seen patients who demonstrated the pseudo-virility phenomenon, and I must say my response to them was somewhat different. I have seen a thousand patients with pain in the chest who feared they had heart disease, and I was able to give them the assurance, at the completion of study, that there was all reason to believe that this was not heart disease. I did not think less of the patient who brought this concern to me, for that is what he should do. We judge the patient who magnifies his ills only by the way he responds to our assurances about his ills, and it is only the patient who persists in his anxieties in spite of our assurances who becomes a problem deserving of deeper analysis.

But, on the other hand, these pseudo-virile individuals, who really have heart disease, who really have pain in their chest related to heart disease, present a different kind of problem. I think I have had three of them, and the response was identical: "Doctor, I decided that if this pain really were related to my heart, and I knew that it was brought on by walking, that if I walked far enough it would kill me, so I just set out and walked, and walked, and walked. And the pain got so intense I thought I couldn't bear it, but it didn't kill me, so it can't be heart disease."

Now, I hold that not to be well-guided treatment, but I must say that this pseudo-virility provoked a certain admiration in me, Midwestern boy that I am, reared with a respect for Spartan courage. I had a high regard for these fellows, I must say, even though I did have to end up telling them they had performed the wrong therapeutic measure.

Dr. Hiltner talked about phenomena of universal significance, and I found great satisfaction in his presentation. I would remind you that the schism between those who would deal with illness on the basis of the individual and those who would deal with it on the basis of the community and the family is age-old. I have a great deal of regard for the teaching of Ezekiel who said that a man should deal with his own responsibilities; that the sins of the fathers may be visited upon the children, but that, wherever they come from, it is the individual's responsibility to deal with them.

In the husband-wife relationship, for instance, you have a choice. How are you going to deal with those terrible inadequacies in your partner? Well, either you both can go and have counsel and find out why you behave the way you do, or you can individually reach that maturity which says, "My love for my partner is so great that I won't try to change him. I now love the things that are different from what I once thought they should be." I see the necessity for this approach to the solution of some of our problems, and I think Ezekiel gave it theological foundation.

III. The Effects of Specialization on the Treatment of the Whole Man

Melvin A. Casberg

Our attention in this presentation focuses on two modifying terms used in the title, the first relating to a form of medical practice, and the second to a concept of man as a multidimensional yet potentially complete being. A degree of polarity exists in the very definitions of the two words under consideration. The term "specialization" carries the connotation of a fractionation of interest with a concentration on a part of the total unit. In contrast, the word "whole" in this context denotes a concept of the wholeness or totality of a multistructured unit. Thus we are commissioned by the title of this presentation to explore the effects of a method of medical practice which by virtue of knowledge in depth, but not necessarily in breadth, concentrates on a particular structural or functional part of the whole patient.

The Roots of Specialization

Specialization in medicine became inevitable when the horizon of medical knowledge was extended over too broad an area for the comprehension of one person. With the continued and increasing momentum of medical research we have every reason to believe that this trend not only will accelerate but further splinter the practice of medicine into narrower and narrower segments of interest. Over the past three decades medical college statistics have portrayed a growing interest in specialty practice, with steadily increasing percentages of graduates extending their education into specific residency programs.

In more recent years, by virtue of the growing demands on medical aptitudes, even the general practitioner or family physician is evolving into a specialist. This past year, 1966, the House of Delegates of the American Medical Association defined the general practitioner as a personal physician, oriented to the whole patient, practicing both scientific and humanistic medicine. They urged that this specialty have primary and major board certification with a residency program requiring three to four years.

The growth of specialization directly relates to the explosive expansion in the fields of science, and this changing pattern makes available highly specialized and efficient techniques of medical care. The effect of the burgeoning wealth of medical knowledge and the growing skill of its technical application in diagnosis, prevention, and cure has had a profound influence on the health statistics of our nation. Scourges which within the past century decimated populations almost overnight no longer stalk the land. Medical science, having conquered in large part the epidemic threats to mankind, presently explores and functions in the more sophisticated arenas of human disorders. Stories of the miracles of medicine have become almost commonplace in our news media of today.

The Cost of Specialization

In spite of these substantial and dramatic accomplishments a certain uneasiness pervades the collective conscience of medicine. While on the one hand the pleasant warmth of achievement and justified pride of progress give a sense of fulfillment, there lurks just off the stage of medical action the haunting specter of an asymmetry in the physician-patient relationship, an increasing awareness of the loss of a clear image of the dignity and totality of man. We do not intend here to derogate medical achievements nor to mouth nostalgic references to the horse-and-buggy doctor with his well-intentioned but often inadequate efforts. Yet one would be remiss not to note that this dignified and respected physician of the past, working in an ethos of compassion and human understanding, created a sense of trust and confidence, catalysts which initiated healing reactions beyond those which might be expected from the mere sum total of therapeutic ingredients.

The practice of medicine is an ingenious blending of a scientific as well as an artistic element. The former relates to the factual and largely material knowledge discovered by scientists of the past and present and forged into increasingly effective instruments of diagnosis, prophylaxis, and therapy. The latter, the art of medicine, is the more fragile and personal element pertaining to the application of the science of medicine. To an alarming degree we have witnessed an erosion of the art of medicine, until today, far too often, the patient is lost in a welter of mechanical gadgetry focusing ingeniously on vital fractions of a bewildered and often frightened whole. Professor Mach, in discussing the dangers of impersonal medical practice at an international conference in Geneva, stated, "Where the sensitive and gentle hand of the doctor used to touch the patient's skin, now we have the cold and polished chrome steel surface of the electrical explorer." [1]

In the earliest recorded history of medicine there was very little science and an abundance of art. The priest-physician used his spiritual resources to combat the evil spirits of disease, using incantations and administration born in the mists of ancient superstitions and frequently dispensed in an atmosphere of the grotesque calculated to impress the supernatural and awe the human. Even today in certain parts of the world the understanding of sickness and health has advanced but little beyond the concepts of ancient times.

In January, 1941, my wife, our two children, and I sailed for India, where I was to run a mission hospital.[2] It lay far off the beaten path in the jungles of Berar Province. The Umri Hospital had been built by my father, an architectural missionary, about 1925. Unhappily, the Mission could then get neither funds nor a physician to run the institution, so it had never been used. Modern medical science had yet to reach this province, and endemic and epidemic diseases were unchecked.

When I arrived at the Umri Mission Station, where I had spent much of my childhood, I was still in a quandary as to how modern medicine might best be introduced into the area. For here man's physical and mental conditions were not held to have mere earthly causes. They were all caused by the mysterious operations of whatever power had the upper hand in the constant battle between the legions of good and evil for the control of man.

[1] René Mach, "Médicine scientifique et respect de la personne," *Journal de Genève,* September, 1952.

[2] Cf. Melvin A. Casberg: "Surgeon at the Sacrificial Altar," *Medical Economics,* June, 1957.

The whole future of the mission project would depend on the reaction of the superstitious natives to their first contacts with the hospital. Years of planning and building could come to naught should they fear, resent, or distrust our purpose.

But soon many patients were making their way to the hospital. Most were in dire need of medical care. Others were mainly bent on satisfying their curiosity. Any local fear of our intentions soon seemed to have been dispelled.

Our next step was to find a suitable case with which to demonstrate the benefits of surgery. Removing an appendix or even a good portion of the stomach would mean little to these natives, who lived in and about the jungles and could boast scars far greater than those required for even the most extensive surgery.

Then one day the ideal patient presented herself, seeking relief from a very large and deforming goiter. A custom in many Indian mission hospitals was to have a near relation or responsible friend of the patient sit in a corner of the operating room to witness the surgical procedure. In an area of relative illiteracy, where signed operative permits would be little understood, this observer fulfilled such a legal requirement.

From the moment that it was explained to the nephew of the little old woman with the goiter that he would be privileged to witness the surgery, I had an ardent and enthusiastic supporter. In fact, the preoperative delay of a few days to prepare the patient was a great irritation to this young man who had become so important a part of the surgical team.

Immediately following the surgery, the nephew hurried home and gathered all the villagers about him to hear the story. The men squatted on the ground in close semicircles before the narrator, while the women, children, dogs, and cattle made up the rear echelon. One of the mission school teachers happened to be in the audience. The next morning he gave me a detailed account of the dramatic presentation.

The young nephew had missed little, and his descriptions were accurate. But his attempted interpretations of the acts, quite in keeping with the limits of his knowledge and the locally accepted philosophy of health, were the wonderfully interesting part of it: "I was taken to the temple of healing where, after being gowned in holy white robes and my face and head covered, I was led to the Holy of Holies and seated in a corner.

"The presence of the gods in the sanctuary was so overpowering that not only I but everyone entering hid his face and covered his head.

"The Doctor Sahib came into the Holy of Holies and washed his unclean hands for many minutes in a ritual of purification. Between washings he anointed his hands with oil." (Anointing with oil being a time-honored religious rite, it was only natural that the observer mistook for oil the liquid soap squirted on my hands by a dispensing machine.)

"Then there came into the room a priestess who sat at the head of the sacrificial altar and invoked the blessing of the gods." (To me, a surgeon, such a definition of the operating table was startling, to say the least!)

"After this she breathed upon my aunt and caused her to fall into a deep slumber." (In the book of Genesis we read of the Lord breathing life into Adam. This concept occurs frequently in the Orient, especially in reference to the transference of supernatural powers. Hence, the nephew saw the anesthetist with her apparatus, bowing over the patient's head and talking in low tones, as a priestess chanting her incantations and breathing into the nostrils of the recumbent aunt. What a delightful name for an anesthetist—a priestess of sleep!)

"When my aunt was deep in slumber, the Doctor Sahib slit her throat from ear to ear as a sacrificial gesture, trying to appease the gods with her blood. He and his assistant priests wrestled with the evil spirits for a long time. The strain of the battle was so great that the Sahib's forehead became wet with perspiration and a priestess mopped his brow many times. Finally the evil spirits were overcome and so they rushed from the neck of my aunt, leaving her no longer possessed."

Thus ended the surgical drama—a thyroidectomy in modern medical parlance, but a battle between the gods and the evil spirits when seen through the eyes of an Indian villager.

The sophisticate or cynic may argue that the art of medicine will not diagnose a pancreatic tumor and, when diagnosed, much less be able to remove it. Such a response misunderstands the basic issue of our discussion, namely that, with the expanding body of medical knowledge and the growing emphasis on specialization, medical practice is of necessity focusing on ever narrowing segments of an increasingly neglected whole. Such a focus tends to produce an asymmetry of medical practice which may compromise its effectiveness.

Szilagyi, in his presidential address before the North American Chapter of the International Cardiovascular Society, recently stated,

> Removing the art of medicine from its practice reduces it to a craft that may remain superbly efficient, but cannot retain its

claim to its traditional moral gentility. If the moral quality is subtracted from medicine, it becomes a branch of zoology with a ridiculously exaggerated preoccupation with a single animal species.[3]

Understanding the Whole Patient

Specialization per se does not exclude the art of medicine as an ingredient in its practice; but essential to the fruition of the art is an appreciation and understanding of the whole patient, as well as the dedication of adequate time for its application. All too often the heavy demands of practice and a narrow sphere of interest work against the art of medicine. A former psychiatric patient is quoted in *Lancet* as writing after his discharge from the hospital, "I was chiefly struck by the godlike detachment of the hospital physicians. They thought they could cure anything with drugs and shock, in much the same way that a mechanic tackles engine repair. Some sign from the doctors that they understood how you feel would be of great help." [4]

The inherent dangers of overspecialization have been a concern not only of the present but of antiquity as well. Neubauer points this out in quoting Socrates as saying, "The reason for the frequent failure of Greek doctors is their inadequate knowledge of the whole, the health of which is a necessary condition of that of the part." [5] Tournier, the eminent Swiss physician, in more recent times writes,

[3] D. Emerick Szilagyi, "In Defense of the Art of Medicine," *Archives of Surgery,* 91: 708-9 (November, 1965).

[4] "What the Patient Felt: Personal Papers," *Lancet,* 1:361 (February, 1966).

[5] Vinzenz Neubauer, "Der Weg zur Persönlichkeit" (Innsbruck-Viena: Tyrolia Verlag, 1947).

The need to specialize accords priority to the organ over the organism, turning medicine into a brilliant technique, automatized down to the last detail. Nothing, in my opinion, would be more serious than that the medicine of the person should come to be considered as a supplementary field of specialization reserved to a few rare doctors.[6]

Not only may the effectiveness of therapy suffer as the result of overspecialization, but also that of the precursor of accurate therapy, namely diagnosis. Disease, be it degenerative, infectious, neoplastic, or other, rarely limits itself to the confines of a structural or functional segment of the human body. Thus the specialist, whose knowledge may have great depth in a particular facet but lacks breadth, may not have available that broader source of information so necessary for early and accurate diagnosis.

What may have seemed thus far to be an unreasonable criticism of the specialist should not be construed as such. Specialization as a form of medical practice is not only inevitable, it is also the most effective means of exploiting the explosive scientific discoveries of our age in their skillful application toward bettering the health of mankind. Parenthetically, as a specialist I am exposed to all the criticisms outlined in this discussion. The purpose of this evaluation relates to the necessity for a constructive and objective appreciation of certain inherent weaknesses in this form of medical practice, the most significant of which is the loss of focus on the whole man due to the growing consideration of the finer details of his many and intricate parts.

[6] Paul Tournier, *The Meaning of Persons* (New York: Harper & Row, 1957), pp. 43-44.

The Whole Man

Let us turn now to a consideration of the implications of the descriptive phrase we already have used several times, namely, the whole man. The human being is a mysterious and amazing triad of body, mind, and spirit, who, according to Holy Writ, was created in the image of God. The whole of man is far greater than the simple sum total of his individual fractions, and to approach him merely in terms of one of these segments is to compromise the concept of the dignity of the human being.

Through the years, and particularly in the past century of scientific progress, there has been a keen interest in the philosophical evaluation of man. Various advocates have espoused positions within a spectrum of concepts, ranging from the humanistic to the materialistic. Humanism envisions man as oriented toward a system of values which in turn form a basis of judgment determined by his responses to these values. Materialism establishes man as a part of nature and describes him as fitting into a complex of laws which in general are predictable and of a neutral character.

We note certain truths in both the humanistic and the materialistic philosophies of life. The prudent scientist, while recognizing the beneficial results of science, will at the same time appreciate the fact that there is something more than pure science. The neutrality of materialism is self-evident, for it adapts itself passively to the aims and purposes of human beings. This very subservience makes it foolish to speak of the god of science, for under man's guidance science lends itself with impartiality both to the healing offices of medicine and the destructive instruments of war.

During the Second World War, I served for a time with

a roving band of guerrillas behind enemy lines.[7] My interpreter, a Communist physician, and I had ample opportunity for protracted discussions as we hid in caves or camped in the mountains between periodic military forays. In debates in which we set forth or defended our individual philosophies of life, my materialistic friend would express repeatedly his amazement that I, a man of science, could believe in anything that could not be demonstrated by scientific standards of proof. He prided himself on his staunch belief in only those things which could be tested in the exacting crucible of laboratory research or solved by the precise intricacies of a mathematical formula.

One sunny afternoon as our motley band of warriors rested on the side of a mountain, my interpreter-physician informed me that we had been surrounded by the enemy and our position was most precarious. Plans called for an attempted dash through this encirclement after dark. Letters home might be written and hidden safely, to be recovered later and forwarded to loved ones in the event of death.

As I sat writing a farewell letter to my wife and children, each breath of air, each glint of sunlight on the sparkling mountain stream, each copper-tinted autumn leaf, each cascading warble of the birds, each sigh of the wind became crystallized into something a thousand times more beautiful and sweet when viewed in the perspective of life and death. My Communist friend sat a stone's throw away, deeply engrossed in the bitter-sweet task of composing words which might be a final communication with his wife and children.

In the midst of writing I paused to interrupt my com-

[7] Cf. Melvin A. Casberg, "For Affliction Does Not Come from the Dust," *California Medical Journal,* 104:381-86 (May, 1966).

panion's reflections. I asked whether the significant thoughts embodied in his composition could be proved in the test tube or on the blackboard. His answer was an averted look, for he knew as well as I did that our most profound thoughts in the face of the impending crisis were not related to the material things of life, nor could they be measured by the tools of physical exploration. There were neither qualitative nor quantitative tests that could evaluate accurately our intimate personal experiences of love, hope, or faith.

Man is not the victim of a horrendous scientific joke, living a life without purpose and operating under purely material laws. He has demonstrated the power of faith, and it is because he believes in something beyond himself that he has progressed to where he is today. Justice Holmes spoke succinctly to this point as follows, "Life is a roar of bargain and battle, but in the very heart of it there rises a mystic spiritual tone which gives meaning to the whole." [8]

We return to the interpretation of the whole man as a composite of physical, mental, and spiritual facets, each essential to his total well-being. The wise physician appreciates this mystical composition and realizes that the material or physical master key alone cannot unlock all the storehouses of health. Furthermore, he interprets health in its broadest concept to include all three of these essential facets, for to heal the body in the face of a broken mind or spirit is a partial victory at best.

Specialization Affects the Specialist

Thus far we have centered our thoughts on the effects of specialization on the patient. Let us turn to a brief considera-

[8] Oliver Wendell Holmes, *Speeches* (1918), p. 103.

tion of how this method of practice affects the specialist, first in his educational preparation and then in the application of this in his later professional life. The long years of institutional residency training with their intensive scientific concentration are not always conducive to the development of a strong physician-patient orientation. When the specialist commences private practice he is a middle-aged man with a fixed pattern of action, a pattern molded in large part in an environment characterized by group rather than personal responsibility for the patient.

The artificial departmental boundaries of some residency programs tend to mold the resident into narrow medical patterns, rather than attempting to fit the pattern to the resident. The following story warns of the tragic dangers of fitting all residents into a single academic mold:

Once upon a time the animals decided they must do something heroic to meet the problems of a "new world." So they organized a school. They adopted an activity curriculum consisting of running, climbing, swimming, and flying. To make it easier to administer the curriculum, all the animals took all the subjects.

The duck was excellent in swimming, in fact better than his instructor; but he made only passing grades in flying and was very poor in running. Since he was slow in running he had to stay after school and also drop swimming in order to practice running. This was kept up until his web feet were badly worn and he was only average in swimming. But average was acceptable in school, so nobody worried about that except the duck.

The rabbit started at the top of the class in running, but he had a nervous breakdown because of so much work in swimming.

The squirrel was excellent in climbing until he developed

frustration in the flying class, where his teacher made him start from the ground up instead of from the treetop down. He also developed "charlie horses" from overexertion and then got "C" in climbing and "D" in running.

The eagle was a problem child and was disciplined severely. In the climbing class he beat all the others to the top of the tree, but he insisted on using his own way to get there.

At the end of the year an abnormal eel that could swim exceedingly well and also could run a little, climb, and fly a bit had the highest average and was valedictorian.

Let us now consider certain effects of specialization on the specialist himself as he practices medicine. Specialization is a two-way street. It not only affects the patient, it makes an impact on the specialist. An exhaustive understanding of any segment of clinical medicine yields substantial intellectual rewards, both subjective and objective. But when this occurs at the expense of personal exchange and understanding between physician and patient, then both parties must suffer. The physician loses that greatest of rewards, the human warmth of patient respect and gratitude. The patient, on the other hand, is denied the therapeutic catalyst of his physician's personal solicitude. Sad indeed is the circumstance in which therapy is dispensed with no more personal interest in the transaction than that of the scientist conjugating amino acids. And this works both ways. I am not saying that this is a typical example of the specialist. I am being somewhat dogmatic here, because this fear of losing vital human contact is very real. As I talk to medical students, this is an area which I feel needs constant repetition.

When I was dean of a school of medicine several years ago, it was my habit to give a series of lectures to the senior students on the broad ethical aspect of the practice of medicine.[9] In the discussion of the various rewards for professional services I made it a practice to tell these embryo physicians how I received my greatest surgical fee.

The mission hospital, located in the jungle of Central India, was considered by the superstitious villagers as the Temple of Healing, where battles were fought between the evil spirits of disease and the good spirits of health. One day a shikari, or hunter, brought his wife from their home in the jungles. She was seriously ill and in need of immediate surgical care. Fortunately, the surgery and postoperative convalescence progressed quite satisfactorily. The day of departure arrived, and after an invocation calling for the blessing of the gods upon Doctor Sahib, the staff, and the hospital, the shikari lifted his wife on the bullock and then scrambled up in front of her. Soon the two of them, riding bareback tandem, disappeared down the road toward their jungle hut.

From that day until my departure from the mission station several months later, I saw my shikari friend once a week. After completing the morning's work at the hospital I would find him seated on the steps of my bungalow, his bullock tethered nearby.

The weekly visit in itself was no simple task, for the plodding trip by bullock was a full day's activity. I could imagine the shikari on Monday beginning to plan for that week's gift. Sometimes the gift was at hand, something taken from his small store of possessions. Sometimes, with a larder depleted, the hunt was long and tedious. Then would

[9] Melvin A. Casberg, "Knowledge Comes, but Wisdom Lingers," *Journal of Medical Education,* 33:686-95 (September, 1958).

come the long ride and brief visit with the Doctor Sahib.

On my arrival he would stand. Bowing graciously with all the dignity of a maharajah, he would hand me a cloth-wrapped bundle. The partially decomposed rabbit or the not-so-fresh wild fowl eggs wrapped in a dirty piece of cloth were the produce of his labor, gifts of love. In these transactions no bag of jewels were ever handled with greater pomp and care.

After the shikari's departure, I buried these gifts in the quiet of the night, mere refuse in the eyes of the world. Yet as I walked back to the bungalow, the day's accumulation of physical tiredness mysteriously melted away, for in that rag I had been permitted to observe the miracle of love working in the depth of man's soul. This is by far the greatest professional surgical fee I have ever received. At the very heart of medicine lies enshrined the dignity and worth of men. Without such terms of value the practice of medicine becomes as sounding brass and tinkling cymbal.

Thomas Huxley, in a speech before the Royal Academy of London, said:

When men no longer love nor hate; when suffering causes no pity, and the tale of great deeds ceases to thrill, when the lily of the field shall seem no longer more beautifully arrayed than Solomon in all his glory, and the awe has vanished from the snow-capped peak and deep ravine, then indeed science may have the world to itself, but it will not be because the monster has devoured art, but because one side of human nature is dead, and because men have lost the half of their ancient and present attributes.[10]

[10] "Science and Art," Speech delivered at the annual banquet of the Royal Academy in London, on May 5, 1883.

IV. Working with Persons in Crises: An Informal Dialogue

Edward H. Rynearson and
Edward M. Litin

Edward H. Rynearson

In a program of this duration we cannot discuss all the tensions and all the anxieties which may play a role in any family or individual crisis. I am sure that each of us at times has wondered whether it would be possible for anyone to escape from the stresses and strains of everyday life. When Bishop Fulton J. Sheen and I presented a dialogue before the American Medical Association, I asked him whether anyone had made a study of nuns who belong to a cloistered order, or of priests who had joined a monastic order with vows to silence and practical isolation, to find out whether these individuals who had been more or less removed from the mainstream of life had fewer "functional complaints," fewer tension symptoms, than individuals who are in the marketplace, so to speak.

Bishop Sheen said that to his knowledge there never had been such a study, and that if one were made he would have no interest in it. He said: "I'd have no interest in it because you would have to tell me why this girl joined a cloistered order, or why this young man joined a monastic order. Why doesn't this priest want to do what I do?" I think the Bishop had a very good point, and I doubt whether we could solve our problems simply by withdrawal from life. (More likely we might create some *added* problems.)

On this blackboard I have drawn a familiar series of concentric circles with the individual in the center and his relationships to the enlarging circles of home, community, international, and spatial relationships. In this informal dialogue Dr. Litin and I will be talking first about the individual, and all of us know that an individual's life may be determined right at the moment of conception. The nature of the conception itself sometimes produces an emotional crisis. Let us first discuss the crisis of a pregnancy resulting from rape. I am going to do whatever I can to force each of you in this audience to personalize some of these experiences, and the girl we are talking about now is *your daughter*.

The girl is sixteen years of age, and she was abducted by a group of men. She was kept in a cabin for ten days before she was finally rescued and brought back to your home and your community. She is pregnant and has been raped many times by these bestial men. I have purposely used the figure of ten days since this eliminates any question of the postcoital contraceptive pill. There is no oral medication for her; there is only one question: Is she to have a therapeutic abortion? I have posed this question several times, and as you can imagine, I have received some differing opinions. One opinion was that the trauma for this girl occurred at the time of the rape—"that from here on in, it's just nine months of waiting." At that time the baby will be put up for adoption, "and that's that." I asked these good friends of mine: "Do you mean to tell me that you would not want this pregnancy interrupted in order to save this girl from the complete destruction of her life?" These friends said, "No, if this were a daughter of ours, we would not attempt to interrupt this pregnancy." All right, that is their decision. What is *your* decision for your daughter? Well, I can tell you what my decision would be if this had ever happened to one of my daughters. She most certainly would have had a therapeutic abortion. And we must always make certain that, if this decision has been reached, facilities should be available to have it performed under ideal circumstances in a hospital. This could never have been done in the hospital where I interned, nor in St. Mary's Hospital where I have had forty years of happy association with the sisters who are responsible for it. I do not believe that I have ever during this time done anything in St. Mary's Hospital which would not have had the approval of the sisters, but that does not mean that were this to have happened to my daughter I would not have taken her to another hospital where she could have had the abortion.

Let us consider another situation in which there should be the question of sterilization. A diabetic mother has had three children and is approaching the time for the delivery of her fourth child. Everyone involved in her care is in agreement that her best opportunity to have a live baby is with a Cesarean section. It is the wish of the mother and the husband, and the recommendation of the doctors, that at that time this girl should have her fallopian tubes tied. The obstetrical group concerned with this girl has always had its service only in a Catholic hospital, and this operation could not be performed there. So, with everyone's understanding, this mother would be transferred to another hospital in the community from where following the Cesarean section and the tying off of the tubes she and the infant would be returned to the first hospital. The point I am making is that I think it very important for physicians to have facilities where their recommendations may be carried out—if not in one hospital, then in another.

What is to be our decision for another diabetic mother who has had four children? Her diabetes has always been quite severe, and she has severe kidney failure, marked diabetic retinopathy with her vision badly impaired, and diabetic neuropathy. She is in the first trimester of another pregnancy and has developed toxemia. We know that her chances of living through this pregnancy are very poor. I can't write down on the blackboard how long she will live if we do a therapeutic abortion, but we know that she will likely die unless this pregnancy is interrupted. Her only chance for remaining a wife to her husband and a mother to her present four children is to have a therapeutic abortion. In my capacity as a physician interested in diabetes, I have been faced with this problem and I have voted for an abortion. As everyone in this audience knows, this is never a single decision; there are many other physicians whose opinions will be secured, and quite obviously not all physicians can agree in each instance.

Not all decisions are black or white, and if we move into the gray area of choice we might consider the problem of thalidomide with its high percentage of malformed babies. If a woman has taken such medication and is pregnant, this whole problem of a therapeutic abortion must receive discussion. Physicians must remember that if the possibility of a malformed baby has not been discussed with the patient and her husband and if a malformed baby results, the physician can be sued. At this time there is a suit before the New Jersey State Supreme Court because the family charged that the physician did not discuss with them the problems posed by her having had German measles early in the pregnancy. The parents charged that they were lulled into a false sense of security, and that the physician precluded them from seeking independent advice or arranging for a therapeutic abortion, and the baby was malformed and mercifully dead.

Before I turn the microphone over to Dr. Litin I wish to reemphasize my determination to do all I can to make certain that each of you at these discussion tables, after you return to your own communities, will approach these and other comparable crises in a most personalized fashion. Each of us must say in every instance, "What would I have wanted done if this were a close relative of mine?"

Edward M. Litin

I do want to elaborate on a couple of points that were made by Dr. Rynearson in regard to the young girl who was raped. For one thing, I've heard all too often a very glib explanation: "Well, if she doesn't want to keep the baby, let the baby be born and adopted out," as if that were the end of the whole affair. Quite the contrary, because we not only see these individuals in crisis right at the time but in subsequent years as well, we observe the agony, the guilt, the great anxiety which they suffer after adopting out such an infant. They have a great sense of responsibility and a feeling of rejection and guilt as a result of having given up their child.

We often try to determine from such individuals whether there would have been as much guilt, or as much thought given to the entire affair, had the pregnancy been terminated right at the time that it was discovered. Invariably the answer is "No." Let me just point out that the poor girl, who has no real culpability in this situation, cannot win.

Either way she is a loser. Our primary duty is to see to it that this individual suffers as little as possible. We are faced, not with abstractions or statistics, but specific individuals who are confronting us in the office, in crises. They are hurting, they are in a great deal of pain. They come to seek help. Now, it is one thing to be able to sit back and philosophize at your leisure about future developments, about things that may happen twenty years from now. Unfortunately, these situations often require action here and now. Admittedly, things would be much easier if we were not confronted with such situations, but we are, all too frequently.

When a decision like this has to be made, I'm not the least bit interested in statistics. I'm not interested in how many girls commit suicide as a result of the fact that they are pregnant and could not obtain an abortion. I'm much more interested in this individual girl sitting in my office at the time. I don't want to be bound by specific or general rules that are supposed to apply to each and every individual case. No two people I've ever met are alike in their emotional response, in their personality makeup, and so on.

I would like to feel that we have sufficient leeway to make what we think is a good medical decision, one offering the greatest protection for the individual who is sitting in our office right at the time. This is the person who comes to us for help. We have to evaluate her overall situation, plus our own situation and her relationship to her family, to her children who are already existing. We must try to determine what is the best course of action to take with this type of individual. As I am pointing out, it's a double-edged sword. There is guilt in either direction. There is suffering and mental anguish in either direction. If the pregnancy is allowed in this young girl, who is the victim of multiple rape, then she suffers a great deal of guilt about adopting out such a child. Throughout life she may ask: "Should I or should I not have adopted that child out? After all, it was my child. Where is that child now? I wonder what type of care is being given to my baby?" On the other hand, admittedly there is guilt if a therapeutic abortion is undertaken. I would like to be able to evaluate which would be the least destructive solution in such a situation, rather than be bound by some particular general rule which says always or never, and which can never really apply in all situations.

Of course philosophical concepts are involved, and our own morals enter into this very strongly. I, at least, prefer to think that we do have moral views that enter into the decisions that are made. But the one thing that does affect my decision very strongly is that I am much more interested in the living people right here and now: the girl in my office, her father, her mother, her brothers, her sisters, her husband if she's a married woman, her children who are already existing. I am much more interested in evaluating their overall situation than in someone who is not existent at the present time. This takes us perhaps into the next subject, that of abortion in general.

You cannot pick up any kind of periodical now without finding some article on the whole subject of abortion. We see cases very frequently of unwanted pregnancies. I'm not talking about unwed mothers, necessarily, but about respectable married women who have a fine family of four or five small children, who find themselves unexpectedly and undesirably pregnant. When one goes into their history, one may find that on one or two of the previous pregnancies they've had some emotional decompensation.

A certain woman, for example, will indicate that if she has to go through another pregnancy, she's positive in her own mind she cannot make it. One finds that she is suffering from great dependency needs, which may give her a great deal of difficulty in emotionally caring for the already existing children. To burden her with another one may very well cause some degree of decompensation. It is not a matter we determine lightly, as though we were worried that it might interfere with her bridge dates or her luncheon dates or her other schedules. It is a matter of her ability to exist in her own world with such great dependency needs. Now she finds herself burdened again with the impending birth of a child, plus the horrifying fear of the possibility of a psychotic decompensation, which she may have undergone in the past.

This is the type of situation we may label a crisis. Some decision must be made as to whether one can recommend interruption of this pregnancy or not. Of course the simplest thing is to say very glibly: "Well, carry it though pregnancy and adopt it out." This is the easy way out as far as the doctor is concerned, but I'm not sure we're doing the patient and her family any great service. Again, I say, these are always double-edged swords. There is guilt on either side. One cannot win a hundred-percent victory either way, but I think there should be some freedom of choice in regard to the particular tack that one wants to take in this type of case.

We might discuss various other cases. I remember a case where the husband was in the navy and due to come home about one year after having gone away. The wife comes in pregnant about a month before he is due home, obviously quite distraught. She is acutely suicidal and cannot face her husband or the whole situation if she is pregnant. Well, personally I'm in no position, nor do I desire to be in the position, of moralizing with this girl, telling her that she must be punished for her sin, or anything like that. I'm much more interested in seeing what can be done for this young lady, for her husband who will also suffer a great deal under the circumstances, and for any children that she has at the present time. So this is far from a very simple question but again shows the type of decisions that can and oftentimes must be made without resorting to all sorts of generalizations that might allow one to feel more comfortable.

Dr. Rynearson

Dr. Litin, may I interrupt you, please? Since we are trying to personalize our presentation, I would like to talk about a very real crisis posed by a lovely woman whose husband was due to come back from a year of foreign service. She had found that she was between one and two months pregnant. She more or less laid down the ground rules herself by saying, "Now there are a few things I don't want you to discuss with me. I don't want you to tell me that my husband will be understanding; believe me, though he is a very wonderful man, he wouldn't be understanding about this situation. Don't tell me that I could go ahead and have this baby and that we could work things out. Instead let me tell you something. Either we work out some way for me to have a therapeutic aborton, or I'm going to kill myself." I am sure all of us as medical or spiritual advisors have heard people threaten suicide when we knew perfectly well that they were most unlikely to do so. But this very intelligent and very determined woman was very serious, and I knew perfectly well that the only way to save her life was to help her have a therapeutic abortion.

Now this is a "gray zone" where within this audience we would have widely divergent opinions. But again speaking for myself, I can only report that I helped make arrangements for her to have this abortion in an excellent hospital far from her home, and that some months later I received a letter from her saying that her husband had returned and that they were happily reunited.

Dr. Litin

A couple of other subjects are well worth dealing with. One is that of the problem of acute and chronic illness, especially involving elderly people. Consider the elderly parent who is being cared for, usually, by a daughter. We see this type of problem very frequently, and there is a crisis here as far as the daughter is concerned. I've seen so many cases where the daughter is ridden with a great deal of guilt because of entertaining death wishes toward the aged parent. I defy anyone in this audience to show me the case of a long-standing chronic illness in a very aged individual that requires a great deal of care, in which the relatives have not at one time or another entertained death wishes toward him. Unfortunately, so many people are riddled with tremendous guilt that is almost paralyzing, because such a thought has crossed their mind, not of killing the individual but wishing his death. I think that this, coupled with a great deal of hostility toward the individual, plus the long-standing statement that had been drilled in, that of course you must love a parent, has led to much difficulty, especially in middle-aged women who are charged with the care of an elderly parent.

This represents a crisis for these individuals. So many of them cannot possibly part with the parents and put them in a nursing home, even though it's the most logical thing in the world to do. Intellectually they can see that this is the natural course of events, but emotionally they cannot bear to make this type of break. I think such individuals need help in making this type of decision, and support after they have made it. If they cannot take this step, they will still need a great deal of emotional support. Someone in a position such as the pastor occupies, or the doctor, can give them emotional comfort. A friendly hand, an understanding of the feelings that they go through, an appreciation that it is not all roses, is what they need. And they need to understand that it is not all love that transpires, that there is a great deal of hostility, sometimes very subtle, sometimes very unaware, but nevertheless a great deal of hostility that interacts among the members of this family. This can have a rather fraying effect, unless the individuals involved have an opportunity to discuss these feelings with someone such as a pastor, or a doctor.

Dr. Rynearson

I would like to step from a discussion of crises to the very frequent problem of the effect of nervous tension. I don't know what percentage of patients comes to the Mayo Clinic because of symptoms which have no basis in any organic disease that our institution can find. I am quite certain that every physician on our staff and all the other physicians in this room would agree that the figure must be over fifty percent—and some of you would favor a much higher figure. Certainly well over ninety percent of headaches are on the basis of tension. This figure would be lower for patients with gastrointestinal symptoms—patients with real abdominal distress and without any organic disease we can find with any of our tests or with exploratory surgery. Such situations are difficult not only for the patients but also for the physicians; gallstones are so much easier! I have always been interested in the differing reactions from patients as I attempt to reassure them, and in many instances a woman may say, "You mean to tell me I've come all this distance and spent all this money, and you're trying to tell me that my trouble's in my head?" And I say, "No, ma'am, there's no question about where your pain is; it's in your belly. I'm not arguing that point. But what I am trying to get you to see is that you can have that much real distress as the result of 'life'—and I am pleased to reassure you that we find no evidence of gallstones, ulcer, cancer, or other organic disease." The next question from her may very well be, "Just what am I going to tell my husband?" To this patient it is a little less than honorable to have real distress and not have organic disease—"functional distress" is interpreted as a form of weakness.

I probably will never get around to it, but I have often said I would like to write an article entitled "Parsonage Problems." We have more than a thousand pastors or their wives here every year as patients, and it is astounding how many of the pastors' wives are having distress because the parsonage is plastered against the side of the church. The choir may rehearse there, infants may be kept there during the church service, the brownie troop may meet there—and if anyone gets sick during the church service he is brought to the parsonage to vomit. (When Bishop Sheen and I were discussing this informally, he said, "Well, that is at least one problem we don't have!")

The laymen responsible for the church have no right to deny the pastor, his wife, and their children a home and a life which is their own. If I were a pastor I would never go to a church where my wife would be an unpaid member of the staff and our home only an auxiliary church structure. I haven't done nearly as much as I should as a layman in the First Methodist Church here in Rochester. But one thing I did: I used all my energy and influence to have the old parsonage moved away and our pastor provided with a real home in a residential area. In my opinion the laymen in many churches are unchristian in their thoughtlessness toward their pastors.

Dr. Litin

We should mention one other fact before we reach a conclusion: no one should have the impression that crises are all bad.

Crises are not all bad. This is a very fortunate thing, because it does point up our inadequacies. We all can accept the fact that we cannot always be helpful in a crisis, in the sense of actively doing something to assist someone. We feel in psychiatry that by being able to listen objectively to the individual who is sharing with you his feelings, his mental anguish, his anxiety, his depressions, his fears—being able to accept this and discuss it, but, more important, to listen to it—this in itself helps a great many people to face their crises.

But crises are not always bad. You can think of many instances in your own lives or those of your acquaintances where crises have brought an element of strength with them. Unfortunately, these are played up a little more often than is justified. Nevertheless, it is true so often that we should remember that you do not have to do something to end every crisis that an individual may face, even if you could do it. It is incumbent upon us to reduce suffering as much as possible, but that does not mean that we have to do something extraordinary in reducing or terminating the crisis. Many times an element of strength may be gained through the individual weathering a period of crisis, and hopefully mastering this crisis without too much difficulty. It lends a great deal of strength to such a person's ego, to his self-esteem, to be able to survive a period of crisis.

In many situations we cannot do anything specific to end a crisis. We might talk about suicide, for example, a situation in which the entire family finds itself in terrible crisis. So many of our efforts are oriented toward the individual who comes to us. But we are also very much interested in the family. How often we see individuals who have been deeply scarred by the fact of a suicide in the family. I seem to echo the word "guilt" all the time, but this is such a destructive type of emotion. I do not say that all guilt is bad. I think that some guilt is really quite necessary and very desirable. But I am talking about the neurotic type of guilt, that has no genuine basis in fact. Neurotic guilt is one of the most destructive, wasteful emotions we know. We see families that are racked with unrealistic guilt in the case of a suicide in their midst. They remember everything they may have said that may have prompted this suicide. They ask: "Why wasn't I nicer back through these months? Surely I am responsible for the suicide." So they feel guilty in this way, in addition to the shame and embarrassment.

They are people in crisis, as the individual was just before he committed suicide. We must use every means at our disposal to try to prevent suicide, but once it happens, our efforts have to be directed toward the family. Not only do they feel guilty about the suicide, they also feel guilty about the fact that they are furious with the member of the family who committed suicide. Their anger rises because they all too often recognize that suicide was an act directed at them individually.

In this as in many other forms of crisis, the family enters in. We have to be able to recognize the feelings that are extant in the entire family group and concentrate our efforts on them in terms of alleviating their guilt. Much more important than "doing something" to alleviate the crisis is the mere fact that we are interested, listening, and can be objective, sympathetic, and understanding. You have no idea how much help this is to such persons.

Oftentimes we are called into psychiatric consultation by one of our colleagues, to go in and discuss a case with the patient. Oftentimes we walk in, introduce ourselves to the patient, and tell him, "I'm from the Department of Psychiatry. Dr. Rynearson felt that perhaps you could use some help, or wanted to discuss a particular problem. I'd be very happy to hear what your problem is." Surprisingly enough, we can sit there for a full hour without ever saying another word until, finally: "It was very nice talking to you. I hope that you feel better. Good-bye." And the doctor, an hour later, will come up and say: "What in the world did you say to that person? That woman feels a thousand percent better; she just feels wonderful now. What did you say?" It's almost embarrassing to say, "Not a darned word." Yet it is true. This is the main thing we can offer so many times to people who are in crises—simple understanding—an understanding ear to hear their feeling of anguish. When a patient really needs emotional support, many times verbal communication is not necessary. Nonverbal communication and feeling of support are sufficient.

Dr. Rynearson

Dr. Litin and I decided we would discuss last some ideas regarding death. It is my firm conviction that we as physicians and you as hospital chaplains, pastoral advisors, and ministers ought to do all that is possible to help families accept death as a certainty. We need everyone's help in enabling families to understand that we as physicians should not be asked to keep dead people "alive." It is repugnant to me to see how long we are able to keep a "heart-lung" preparation going with tubes in the veins and the bladder and an oxygen tent as a shroud, with the whole team trying to see how long they can keep this body breathing.

Some years ago *Time* magazine reported that Mrs. Wrigley, widow of the founder of the chewing gum industry, was kept alive for more than five years with never a conscious moment. The same thing can happen right here in Rochester or in any of your communities. We had a woman in a nursing home here who had been stricken with encephalopoliomyelitis, who had been unconscious for more than five years.

With this diagnosis she was eligible for money from the polio fund and had received $26,000.00 during this time. It had, however, been insufficient for the total care involved, and her family was almost bankrupt after contributing about $24,000.00. When I heard of it, I asked the patient's sister whether this treatment was being continued at the insistence of the family. She said no, but that no physician had discussed terminating such care. I told her that if the patient were my sister I certainly would not wish this continued, and she decided to consult a priest. He had a very crowded schedule, but I shall always be grateful for his arranging to see the girl during his noon hour. When she returned I asked what his advice was. She said, "The Monsignor wonders why no one had suggested this before." We moved the patient into St. Mary's Hospital where we made certain that she was kept comfortable and permitted to die with dignity. At autopsy she had no brain, yet there is no reason why she could not have been kept "alive" for another indeterminate number of years.

Again I must insist that you personalize this and decide what you would want done for yourself or a member of your family. Someone has to make these decisions; what about you? When I found one of my dearest friends whose brain had been completely destroyed being kept alive with a tracheotomy tube, an oxygen tent, and all the other aids for the prolongation of life, I talked with his wife and sons and found that they were in complete agreement with me that this was an awful thing to be doing to someone we love. So it was up to me to put an end to this dramatic nonsense and to help my friend die with dignity; it was I who removed the tubes and took the responsibility.

Now, I have not used the word euthanasia. I am not talking about killing somebody. But I do believe that if a patient is riddled with cancer from one end to the other, and physicians have done everything known to science to help him, and everything has failed and the patient is still screaming in pain, then why not stop our effort to prolong this awful situation and make certain that the patient does not suffer? As I have said previously[1]:

"In discussing this conviction, I have received three comments or questions. The first is: 'You are trying to play God.' I reject this charge, for I believe that it is actually the physician who, by using extraordinary measures, prolongs life and suffering who 'plays God.'

"Second is the query, 'What do physicians do?' Well, that has been answered innumerable times, and many of the instances in question are in my own practice and among my own friends. Most physicians do not ask for anything more than kindness and comfort; they are likely specifically to oppose 'heroic measures.' Every physician worthy of the name shrinks from the 'I: It' relationship with his patient and, rather, embraces the 'I: Thou' apposition, for his daily labors remind him only too forcefully that one day he, too, will be the patient.

"Third is the question: 'What would you do if this occurred in your own family?' The travail and misfortune I am speaking about did occur to a member of my immediate family; we kept her in her own bed in her own home and made certain she suffered as little as possible until she was released by death.

[1] E. H. Rynearson, "You Are Standing at the Bedside of a Patient Dying of Untreatable Cancer," CA 9:85-87 (May-June), 1959.

"I conclude by saying that when I am at the bedside of a patient dying of untreatable cancer, I make the decisions I have recorded here. But now YOU are standing at another bedside and YOU must make YOUR decision."

It is only by working together that physicians and spiritual advisors can bring total treatment to the total patient, and there have been occasions when I perhaps have acted both as a physician and a spiritual advisor. When I was interning in Pittsburgh, we were having a terrible epidemic of lobar pneumonia, long before the days of any effective treatment. At that time we had a forty-percent mortality rate in patients who had positive blood cultures. It was 3 a.m. when one of the student nurses came and told me that one of the men who was dying was uncontrollably emotional. I went to his bed in the center of a large ward. He knew he was dying and was terror stricken to die with no member of his family, no friends that could be at his bedside. And he was concerned because he had never been baptized. I ran across the street to our intern quarters and picked up a little Bible bound in pigskin, which had on the flyleaf, "This Bible was purchased on October the 9th, 1919, from Charlie Laughlin, the YMCA Secretary at Ohio Wesleyan." I took the Bible back to the ward and read to him some of the passages familiar to all of us. The nurse screened his bed and brought me a little cup of water, and I baptized him. By what authority? By the authority vested in me by my parents who taught me this faith, by Charlie Laughlin and my other friends at Ohio Wesleyan, and by the authority of my own conviction. It made a tremendous difference to this patient in those last remaining minutes of life, and, interestingly, it made quite a difference in me.

DISCUSSANTS

Howard J. Clinebell, Jr.

We have had a superb illustration in the last hour or so of what Seward Hiltner calls "the pastorhood of all believers"—in the work and spirit of two doctors who are taking their lay ministry seriously. They are doing so in terms of specific sacramental acts (such as the baptism of a dying man which was a tremendous work of mercy and healing in the name of Christ). Furthermore they are implementing their ministry by incorporating in their decision-making what I would regard as the touchstone of the Christian ethic, namely: What is the effect on persons if we go this way or that? For example, What is the effect on the growth and fulfillment of the God-given potentialities of all the persons involved if a therapeutic abortion is performed or is not performed?

I have only this observation about the various kinds of ethical dilemma which were discussed. It seems to me that we would get very little argument from this audience on the rightness—in fact, the obligation from a Christian perspective—of performing therapeutic abortions in the cases described, and of following up the abortions by whatever pastoral counseling or psychiatric help is needed to handle the emotional problems constructively.

Let me raise a closely related issue. It seems to me that as churchmen we have an obligation to be more articulate and more outspoken, and to make more constructive noise in places where decisions are being made. We should be doing more to back up the physicians who have very sensitive consciences on these matters. Too often the church has let the doctors down in not speaking up more forcefully and firmly on questions such as these that have been raised.

We are all facing new ethical dilemmas because of the advances of medicine. We need doctor-clergy-social scientist cooperation in resolving these. Take the new problems posed by longevity, for example, by the fact that medicine can often prolong life for many decades. What is the impact of this medically produced longevity on families? What we need is not just new therapies but also a new ethic for learning to live with the advances that medicine has given us. The middle-class ethic regarding aging parents is an ethic based on the nineteenth century, when most people had farms or large houses and large clans where aged parents could be accommodated for long periods of time without excessive strain on the children and the grandchildren. We need, as churchmen, to do our homework in the field of ethics better and to help develop an ethic that fits the advances of medicine.

One thing that bothered me a bit about the stimulating dialogue we have heard was an implied assumption. It has to do with the issue of how one goes about making decisions in the gray area. I thought I heard our eminent speakers say to their medical colleagues, "It's up to you to get busy and make your own decisions—taking your own stand on an individual basis." My conviction is that the grayer the decision area becomes, the more imperative it is that we do not risk making decisions on an individualistic basis, but rather on a team basis. In this way we cancel out each other's blind spots to some extent. I am thinking of such gray areas as decisions about how long the physical organism should be kept going by medical and mechanical means after hope of recovery seems to be gone. Should any one person be given the power to make such an awesome decision alone? Is not a decision by a panel of experts more apt to be the wise and humane one? What is the role of the clergyman in serving as a consultant on ethics in such a team effort?

On another issue I sense a widespread feeling among ministers with whom I have talked. One of the problems of medical-clerical relationships in dealing with certain fundamental problems in medical care is a difference in understanding how solutions should be approached. Take, for example, the major crisis in the whole field of medical practice in America posed by the fact that approximately forty million Americans are removed from the mainstream of American life, which includes the mainstream of American medicine. I suspect there would be a split of opinion here among many of the pastors and many of the doctors on whether individualized medicine can ever cope with this gigantic social problem which infects the body of our society. Is not the fact that forty million Americans are deprived of full access to the benefit of modern medicine a fact which demands a response on the part of churchmen, a response which hopefully will point toward a realistic solution?

On other medically induced crises the church has been strangely silent. There is, for example, the matter of drug dependency in this age of psycho-chemistry. It has been predicted by pharmacologists and others that in a few years we will have a drug for regulating every state of the human psyche. Many of these, I understand, are already available on the pharmaceutical shelves though not yet released for prescription by physicians. Is the church ready to cope with the Orwellian *1984* implications of the age of mind-altering drugs? Churchmen should help make guidelines for dealing constructively with the revolutionary implications of these mind-transforming drugs. Doctor-clergy cooperation in developing such guidelines is clearly indicated.

The problem of depth communication between pastor and physician is a tough one, and a part of the problem is that we clergymen have not done our homework. That is, we have no clear picture in our own minds as to the unique contributions that we can make to the team approach toward formulating ethics regarding the human problems related to new medical practices. The minister often feels that he is not on the healing team. In fact, he is not even playing the same game. This is probably not as true of the clergymen who are here as it is of clergymen at large. Most of those who are present have had clinical training and have learned how to communicate across professional lines. But I believe it is true that the average parish clergyman does not feel that he is a part of the healing team in the hospital of his community or in the discussions of ethics as related to medicine. I suspect that the ideal situation you have described here at the Mayo Clinic, where clergymen have a role in the decision-making process in these complex areas, is atypical for the country at large. Our goal should be to make it typical.

I do not think we clergymen can afford to wait until the doctors invite us to collaborate with them. After all, we are both dealing with the same people, our parishioners and their patients, and the welfare of these people is our mutual concern. I think we have to take the initiative in getting acquainted and in offering to work with them in any ways we can be helpful to the patient-parishioner.

The unique contributions of the clergyman to the healing team would seem to be in two areas. First, as one trained in thinking systematically about ethics, he should be of special help in the area of complex ethical-medical decisions. Second, as indicated earlier, the clergyman is an expert in spiritual growth. When people face the fact that life itself is a terminal illness, that nobody gets out alive, they face immense spiritual questions. As clergymen, we should be prepared to help people deal with these questions and with what Erik Erikson calls "the ego chill"—the awareness of our mortality. In our own lives the background music that plays constantly throughout our days is the realization that we will eventually die. In moments of crisis the volume gets turned up, but the background music is always there. This music is the context within which we minister to people, in sickness and health, in crisis and noncrisis. The clergyman, if he is trained to integrate the psychological and the theological disciplines, should make a unique contribution to helping people deal with the unique human dimension of humanness: our self-conscious awareness that we are finite, and the problems derived from this for which there are only spiritual answers.

An example, on the national scale, of the way in which the clergyman often is not thought of by the medical profession as a member of the healing team, is the following: The report of the Joint Commission on Mental Illness and Health, *Americans View Their Mental Health,*[2] revealed that more people go to clergymen for counseling than to all the mental health professions combined. Some forty-two percent of all the people who went to any professional

[2] Gerald Gurin *et al.* (New York: Basic Books, 1960).

person for help, a national survey found, chose to go to priests, rabbis, or ministers. This being the case, it is startling that when the most recent commission, the one on Mental Health and Children, was appointed, no clergyman, no one representing the theological perspective, was appointed a member. Yet it is clear that the church plays a powerful role in family life and in influencing the mental health of children.

Doctors, like other laymen in the field of the ministry, tend to misunderstand the dual role of the clergyman in crises. We need to get the message across that if the clergyman is adequately trained he is equipped to do two things to help persons in crisis:

First, he can support the person in handling the pain and frustrations of his situation by offering him the strength and comfort that come from the riches of the religious heritage.

Second, a clergyman can help release the coping potentials, the ego resources, the resources for health and wholeness within the person that have been blocked by the spiritual and psychological barriers in his inner life. It is this second function of which the physician may not be aware. It can be a very significant contribution to the healing team.

Let me mention now what I think to be a part of the solution to the problem of increasing interprofessional dialogue and cooperative clinical training as an integral part of seminary education. Along with ecumenism, the development of clinical pastoral training is one of the most powerful forces transforming American Christendom in our century. One of the many values of clinical training is that it teaches theological students and clergymen to talk across discipline lines and to work as a member of the healing team. Those of us who have influence in theological schools can encourage students to take this training. Hospital administrators and staff members can encourage their hospitals to make it possible to establish an accredited clinical training program by employing a chaplain supervisor. This is one of the ways of advancing clergy-doctor cooperation in crises and strengthening the ability of ministers to participate in interprofessional activities of all kinds.

Amos N. Johnson

For thirty-three years now, I have been rendering health care as a family physician to a captive group of people in eastern North Carolina. I live in a small farming community. We have seven hundred people in the village in which I live, and we've had quite a population explosion. When I went there thirty-three years ago, we had six hundred forty, and the population explosion during the last thirty-three years has moved us up now to seven hundred, so we are doing very well. I tell you this only to let you know that, as the only physician in that immediate area, I have a ninety-eight percent captive audience. We have less than two percent transients. If we hadn't had this last World War and people from my area had not been put in camps in California and married girls out there, we wouldn't have those two percent transients.

I have therefore seen all these problems and seen them from a very intimate association with my patients over these years. I know every person in that area by his first name. I delivered most of them who are less than thirty-four years of age, and in some instances I have been looking after three or four generations of these people. I am familiar with these problems on a firsthand basis.

To get to the discussion of the crises, the only thing that concerns me about the matter of abortions is not the abortions themselves. It is: Did we as good family physicians attempt to prevent the situation that led to the need for the abortion? In the case of the sixteen-year-old girl, obviously, there was not a great deal that we might do. We might try to do something to improve the mores of our community, but that is an unbelievably difficult task. But in the case of the two pregnant women with diabetes, the one that was to have the Cesarean section and the tubes tied, the other to have the abortion to save her life: Should we not first look into the matter of contraception, or some other mechanism of birth control, depending upon your religion, to make sure that everything possible is done to prevent this crisis from arising?

Certainly, we can as Christian physicians talk to many of our patients who want no more children but are perfectly healthy, and help them to work out a mechanism so that they don't make the one slip that winds up with the unwanted pregnancy. However, I am in thorough accord with the decisions that you all did reach here. I also would do the same things that you have done, and I have done them.

I have some convictions about this business of extending life, about a person's right to die. I think a person has a perfect right to die with dignity, and I think that under certain circumstances a patient literally has a right to die when he might live a little bit longer. Less than six weeks ago I had a man in my community who had severe emphysema. He couldn't walk as far as from here to my chair over there. He had bronchial asthma and the heart condition that goes with it, and life to him was a burden. He had often told me that he would like very much to go to sleep one night, and just not wake up the next morning. Well, this was impossible. I adhere to the oath of Hippocrates and I'm not going out and start a euthanasia plant, nor a concentration camp to exterminate part of the human race.

But one Sunday morning this patient cut his wrists, thinking he was doing it without being noticed. His family did catch him and knew enough about first aid to stop the bleeding from the radial artery. It took some fourteen stitches to keep him from bleeding to death. That evening, late, he took the only thing that was accessible to him that he felt might kill him. He had a bottle of digitalis pills which we give those who have cardiac failure. He took fifty digitalis tablets. An hour or two later his wife and daughter discovered it. So, we carried him to the hospital, and we washed his stomach out, and we did everything possible, and he is alive today.

Now, somewhere along the line we need to be able to make decisions, involving not only the pastor and the physician but the conscious patient as well. Not all these patients who wish to die are unconscious. There is such a thing as a person living beyond his age, becoming infirm, and yet while he is relatively still alert getting an air of nostalgia to see his friends, all of whom are dead and gone. If as Christians we believe that there is a better life hereafter, we might in some instances talk with the patient. I have had several of them talk to me. We might under certain circumstances back off gracefully and permit nature to take its course.

We had a wonderful disease when I started practicing thirty-three years ago. Before the advent of the antibiotics and chemo-therapeutic agents, we had a disease, pneumonia, that was known as the old man's friend. Quite often this type of person, in spite of all we could do, would have the opportunity of dying and going on to his reward. I hasten to say that not all people who died of pneumonia had that attitude about it.

I am thinking now in terms of a younger person's right to die with dignity and make his own decision. I had a very dear friend, the wife of the head of the department of a certain medical school, who developed a malignancy at the base of her tongue. She went to an institution in New York, one of the better cancer institutes, and they thought they had removed all of it and had controlled it with cobalt. After coming back shortly from a vacation which she and her husband took, she found that the cancer had returned. She went right back to the same institution, and they suggested that they would like to remove her tongue. She asked the doctor if he would guarantee that if her tongue were removed that she would live and wouldn't die from that particular cancer. He said: "Lady, we can't guarantee you that." She determined that she would keep her tongue, and she went home and died in about two months. That was her decision, and I think that it could be justified.

There are many, many areas where pastors and physicians need to talk together and do it in a leisurely manner over a meal or a golf game. In many instances in communities probably different from mine, it would be better if we assume that the onus is on the pastor to make the first contact with this sort of visit. I believe pastors would find that there are very few primary physicians in the United States who would not be happy to talk with them or their counterparts and work with them on this.

We have a disease which puts up a barrier between the clergy and medicine. We have those in medicine who have become so specialized that they speak a special jargon, and they talk each only to the other and sometimes do not understand their own conversation. A language barrier can develop between the medical profession and those of religion.

One other matter that has concerned me at this conference is that everyone, almost without exception, who has seen the physician and the minister conferring about a patient has assumed the setting will be the confines of the hospital. This to me is a little unrealistic. I submit that it would be better if the minister and the physician became concerned about their community of patients while the patient was being given outpatient care in the doctor's office, or the outpatient clinics, or even at home. Home visits are still being made in some portions of this country, believe it or not.

One problem we have not discussed is that of persons who will not accept medical care under any circumstances. They have a built-in resistance against it, unless it is crisis-oriented. They will come to the doctor only if they are hurting or crippled, and just as soon as the physician is able to get them free of pain and able to manipulate or get about, he does not see them again until another crisis arises. Now, this is not good medical care. These people exist right here in Rochester, Minnesota, where probably the people have access to as good medical care as is existent anywhere in this country.

This is an area, a gray area not concerned directly with

death, where physicians and those who give pastoral services to congregations could work. These people should have someone initiate for them their entrance into the cycle, the provision of medical care. Theoretically it is unethical for a doctor to go out and get a patient by the nape of the neck and the seat of the pants and bring him in off the street. Yet I suspect that good, prospective, preventive care would permit the doctor to tell the clergyman who some of them are and what their potential for trouble is, so that through a mutual effort the two might render better medical care to all their people.

Roy Nichols

I wish to raise some questions, and I speak as a pastor because that is all I know. I have been a pastor all my life. I want to raise some concerns, first on the cases that were cited for us. They raised in me a number of questions concerning the guidelines which the medical doctor is bound to follow.

Out of my own experience as a poor boy growing up in Philadelphia, I can remember how many of us never wanted to go to the hospital because they said they'd give you the black bottle. This fear of the hospital was due partly to ignorance, partly to realism, and was complicated by the factor of race. It caused many of us not to go to the county hospital. Many people died at home who should have and could have gone.

Those days are over, but the thing that kept coming to my mind was that if you had a doctor like Dr. Rynearson making the decision, maybe you would feel good about it. But if any doctor begins to take it upon himself to make these decisions, then maybe we are in trouble. If we take, for instance, the reduction of suffering as an absolute, we could be pushed into supporting even euthanasia. The speakers, representing the entire community both ministerial and medical, have placed before us the seriousness of our position because of our growing medical capabilities.

Hopefully these decisions will not be reached and the guidelines will not be set simply on the basis of wholly immediate considerations, without a framework which supports the judgment. Perhaps we have arrived at the place at which a doctor, who, in addition to his medical knowledge and his desire to reduce suffering, does not have a profound feeling for the spiritual nature of the human being, is not a safe risk in which to invest these tremendous judgments and these responsibilities for decisions.

Some of the ethical dilemmas that were laid before us were more or less open or shut, and we would all agree with them. But I think even these medical men would say they placed before us cases that were more obvious than most. But even with these, I think, we need a broader ethical framework than simply the opinion of the physician relative to the medical urgency involved. Otherwise we cannot preserve for the medical profession the image that traditionally it has enjoyed. A doctor has always been more than just a physiological mechanic or pragmatic specialist who works on ailments.

The second point that I raise is that with the increase in public medicine the doctor-patient relationship changes. In addition to the strictly medical services that are provided by the physician, we have in the past felt the healing presence of the doctor, a certain leisureliness which is a manifestation of his deeper interest in the person as a person. That is the plus therapy in the profession.

Now, as public medicine increases, the doctor is cast in a role where his contact with the patient is satisfactory from a narrowly clinical point of view, but not in the way that he might know the family, the background, the continuity of the people. Do we face the danger that the practice of medicine may become mechanical, especially as it relates to the less affluent segment of the population?

We were talking about the people who come in large numbers to the physician who do not really need the care. But as we move down the socio-economic scales, we see a larger percentage who come long after they need it. These people often get to the doctor months and sometimes years after they should, because of interposing factors of economic circumstance, ignorance of the community network, or suspicion of the services that are available. If the medical practitioner does not extend himself in a humanizing fashion to become more available actually and emotionally to these patients, they will not be reached. We need some kind of program within the medical profession to assure that the doctor remain the kind of human being who has a comprehensive interest in persons. Then the patient will not return from the clinic feeling that the doctor is there only to manipulate him, to make a note and keep a record, but with no profound concern for him as a person.

We are coming to see in America three general categories of people who seek medical assistance: the affluent, represented mostly by the person who can fly to Mayo, request treatment, and stay for the duration. He is intelligent enough to deal with a doctor at the level of his own vocabulary, and his financial means are extensive enough to let him argue with the doctor for weeks and still stay in town.

The second category would be a new crop of what I call "insured people," who through their unions or civil service employment or otherwise are covered by some kind of insurance program. This guarantees them at least the entree to the doctor's office, and ostensibly guarantees payment of the bills up to the limit of their coverage. These people can become the marginal individuals. Coming from the city of New York where everything tends to become impersonal, I recall various experiences with some of the medical plans that cover city employees or individuals in group coverage. One begins to become very shaky about a growing attitude on the part of the medical practitioner toward this kind of "duty medicine," as I would call it. It is not entirely the fault of the doctor; but the doctor, the minister, and the rest of us must do something to rescue medicine and entire health establishments from becoming mechanical and inhumane.

The third category, the people that I know best, are the poor, the people who come too late, the people who are afraid, the people who even more desperately than others need the physician and the minister to be interested in them as persons. We must adjust our approaches as clergymen and as medical men to guarantee that the human element in our treatment extends to all categories of the society. We cannot allow ourselves to be selective in the way we minister to various individuals in crisis.

I am sitting now on the board of directors of the Methodist Hospital in the city of New York, which is the oldest Methodist Hospital in the nation and, I would think, somewhere close to the best.

At the same time, I am sitting on the advisory board of Harlem Hospital in the center of one of the most complex communities in America. Some doctors serve both hospitals. They are graduates of accredited schools and academies. But I see a world of difference in what happens in those two hospitals. I think that preachers, and the medical men themselves, should institute some kind of rebellious group to see to it that healing is not slipshod in some places and thorough in others, especially in relation to the economic circumstance of the client. Crisis for the poor man is crisis, just as it is for the rich and for the insured.

And since we are interested in compassion, we must remember that we are dealing with the health of *human beings*. It takes more than a pill or a surgical removal to heal a human being. The care is more important than the actual therapy itself in some instances.

Finally, I think that we ministers need to recognize, if we desire a closer walk with the physicians, that some of us can't be trusted. (I think some doctors can't be trusted, either.)

The kind of confidential domain that we are inviting ourselves to enter will require, in training men for the ministry, the development of certain disciplines. It is unforgivable, for instance, for a man to use an illustration in a sermon that would in some way jeopardize the shared confidence of a physician in the neighborhood. Especially in dealing with sensitive persons in crisis situations we need to develop this highly confidential rapport between the men of medical science and the men in the ministry. Otherwise we cannot get over this bridge and work effectively at the level of the local community, where the job needs to be done.

V. Medicine's Scientific Developments and Resulting Ethical Problems

Joseph Fletcher

It was first suggested that this paper be entitled: "Scientific Breakthroughs and Resulting Dilemmas in Professional Ethics." But this now seems to me too narrow in some respects and too wide in others. As we shall see, some of the ethical problems posed by medical science are not mere dilemmas but tri-lemmas or even multi-lemmas. Some innovations in recent years are more in the nature of gradual sneakthroughs than sudden breakthroughs. And surely we cannot attempt today to look at the ethical import of *all* scientific work for *all* the professions! Therefore, I am focussing on *medical* science, and the new moral questions it raises for doctors and nurses and the paramedical services in particular, and for those whom they serve—pastors, patients, friends and family, and society. Finally, I speak of "problems" instead of dilemmas, since the latter term often connotes unresolvable issues of impasse, and I am tackling this assignment in a somewhat more optimistic mood. Let me add, by way of parameters and perimeters, that I am not pretending to point to all the ethical problems at stake, but just to some, as a few specifics which give shape and substance to the title.

Let us think of this paper, by the way, as an effort to give the lie to Bernard Shaw's remark in *The Doctor's Dilemma* that "all professions are conspiracies against the laity."

Perhaps many of you know of the present attempt of the

AMA's Department of Medicine and Religion to gather from physicians and clergymen opinions about many ethical questions encountered in the care of the sick. The proposed title of the study is *American Medicine—Ethical and Religious Questions,* and the aim is to cover problems of obligation in managing birth and death, professional ethics, honesty in relationship, secrecy, abortion and illegitimate pregnancies, homosexuality, birth control and artificial insemination, organ transplants, and a host of such moral questions. This phase of our seminar at the Mayo Clinic obviously fits in with the AMA's enterprise.

The term "medical ethics" is used in two ways: (1) to mean a code of manners and guild conduct, and (2) to mean problems of right and wrong, of good and evil, arising in the care of patients and posing issues for patients as well as physicians. It is in this second, broader sense that I shall use the term "medical ethics." It is a subject largely ignored in the curricula of medical schools and in the ethics of Protestantism. Only the Roman Catholic moral theologians and their schools and hospitals treat it with any descriptive and analytical care and competence.

The AMA's Principles of Medical Ethics deal with fraternity or guild obligations, as those of the British Medical Association do. The AMA's Judicial Council rarely deals with nonprofessional problems of conscience. The Council generally assumes the full responsibility of the individual physicians, which is as a matter of fact quite impossible under the interdependence of modern specialization.

In prescientific cultures the medicine man had a priestly and charismatic role. Medicine and religion were closely related prior to modern times. Separated though medicine and religion have become in modern practice, we see a growing person-centeredness in philosophy and psychology. This tends to create a greater interest in ethics than was true of the problem-centered or research-centered approach to the care of patients. Many doctors and nurses tend to see their ethics in terms of Kant's second maxim, to treat men as ends and not as means. As Tillich put it, the "person" is a moral concept.

A Question of Freedom

One of the pervasive issues in medical care is freedom—the question whether people have a right to take their health in their own hands, as the medical sciences and arts are doing where they increase human control over both life and death. This issue arises often in the ethics of reproduction, around fertility control, or with respect to donation of vital organs, such as kidneys or ovaries for transplant to others. Is this an interference with nature, and what kind of theodicy or doctrine of creation and providence is entailed? To what extent have men the stewardship of life and of health? Have they any initiative, or must they abide by "nature's" decree in cases of sterility or loss of vital function or the onset of senility? (Medicine obviously interferes with nature by using nature when it suits human purposes, or outwitting it.) To such questions there are different answers proposed in theological ethics. Until recent years the Catholic view tended to be fatalistic or naturalistic, but of late some personalistic theologians have appeared in their ranks, and according to my bias this is a tendency devoutly to be nurtured.

The greater interest and concern of Catholic theologians

in medical ethics is manifest. They have effective medical guilds (e.g., the Federation of Catholic Physicians' Guilds) and journals dealing with the ethics of medicine (e.g., *The Lineacre Quarterly*). Protestants have no equivalents, although they turn out some magazines and journals which deal with pastoral counseling and care of the sick. If Catholics are ever challenged at any point it is usually with respect to the premises in their somewhat syllogistic arguments, but their careful and thorough knowledge of the medical data and their careful logic are usually beyond reproach.

The story of medical progress traces battle after battle with theological ethics over such matters as human rather than animal anatomical research and study, allowing the heterodox to practice medicine, ectopic excision, craniotomy, artificial insemination, contra-respiration of monsters at delivery, sterilization, therapeutic abortion, anesthesia, contraception, male obstetricians, many such things. Notions such as that "only God gives life," that the body is the "temple" (I Cor. 6), that "nature's way" is God's will, that suffering is redemptive, that nature has intentions and purposes (the "pathetic fallacy"), that vital organs are divine functions, that human mastery over life and living verges on the demonic—such notions are elements in classical theological ethics which have caused much friction with medical science and practice.

Problems from Medical Advances

Most of the problems in medical ethics arise around advances in knowledge and skill. Ethical issues are usually success problems. For example, artificial insemination in some cases of childlessness represents a new remedy for barren marriages, but it also raises questions about the nature of relationship and parenthood (as, indeed, adoption also does). The same is true with contraception, especially the pill and the loop—or the problem of resuscitation and prolonging life beyond senescent levels. We could also mention such issues as the ethics of experimentation (especially clinical), truth-telling in medical diagnosis, non-therapeutic abortion, euthanasia, organ transplants, artificial functions (e.g., electronic and prosthetic cardiac devices), temporary and permanent sterilization, the obligation of doctors to testify adversely in malpractice suits when justified, the integrity of professional confidences in group medical practice, the requirement of the patient's consent for various treatment procedures when often by the nature of the situation competent consent cannot be given. There are many more.

Ethical problems are raised not only by scientific and technical gains. They are also posed by the new structure of medical care. The traditional privacy of relationship is disappearing as medical care becomes more a multiple service by various specialists who exchange information freely. The transfer of a patient from his home to the hospital, from a single practitioner's care to a staff's (the hospital, we must remember, is a medical collectivism), the fact that patients tend to go to the doctor rather than he to them—such things change relationships and values. The enormous cost of modern medicine with its expensive technology and equipment and its costly cadre of professional paramedical personnel (occupational therapists, social workers, hospital staff) creates new ethical problems about socialization and welfare legislation and insurance investment.

The image of the doctor is changing as he leaves the intimacy of general practice for the less personal forms of special service. At the same time his income, especially in America, has increased to nearly the top level for professional people. In plain fact, no competent physician can any longer practice medicine, either in diagnosis or treatment, out of a little black bag, any more than he can get around in a horse and buggy. The profession is really not prepared for these ethical strains, by training or sensitivity. No courses are offered in the ethics of medicine, as distinguished from professional code rules, in any medical school in America or Europe, except for the Roman Catholic schools and teaching hospitals.

We are now moving into the last third of the twentieth century, and judging by the first two thirds we can expect an avalanche of surprises and transforming changes. The first third gave us automobiles, airplanes, World War I, the Soviet Revolution, and the Great Depression. The middle third gave us an end of the old religious and political empires, an even more savage World War II, atomic power, intercontinental rockets, the Chinese Revolution, and a new map of rich and poor nations, uncertain about themselves and one another. Almost all of those born from now on will live most of their lives in the twenty-first century. By 1970 more than half the American people will be twenty-five years old or under. The new generation, like the new nations of the underdeveloped parts of the world, are not interested in the old ideologies that have divided the world of the past. They are concentrating on the practical rather than the ideal, looking for what works rather than for doctrinaire goals. It will be a scientific epoch. Our problems are not the questions in old men's minds but the questions that are in the minds of the young.

Things move very fast. Scientific research and technological innovation seem to proceed in geometric rather than merely arithmetic progression, rather like compound interest, we might say. Sir William Osler's historic contributions to modern medicine are already largely a dead letter, and I recently heard a pharmacologist at the University of Southern California explain how he has to change his lectures to medical students *every semester.*

In some developments there is no ethical problem, or at least no obvious problem. For example, no moral issue is raised by the evidence that allergy can be turned to a good purpose in the treatment of skin cancer by introducing allergy into the cancer cells and then allergizing them to death (so to speak) without harming normal skin tissue.

Other issues arise that are not directly medical but highly relevant, such as the biology of chromosomatic coding, DNA, and genetic control. Real ethical dilemmas are posed here, too. For example, how are we to regard reproduction by a known carrier of a recessive gene for something like pancreatic fibrosis or sicklecell anemia? If such a carrier reproduces by joining with another carrier, the chances are one to four that the children will exhibit the defect. On the other hand, however, if the carrier tries to avoid the danger by somehow finding a noncarrier as prospective mate (this kind of identification is also easier, due to the progress of science), then the couple will actually contribute to spreading the defect ever more widely through society, so that successive generations will find it ever more difficult to find suitable mates.

Overarching Issues of Ethics

We face also what we may call overarching issues of an ethical kind—as whether there is such a thing as the "balance of nature," and if so whether our innovations should be carried out when they might interfere with that balance. Another is the so-called wedge argument against increasing our medical control over vital processes on the ground that every increase of our control increases our power to misuse it as well as to use it creatively. Those who worry about this might say, for example, that we ought not to look for so-called "morning-after pills" to prevent conception and, for the same reason, ought not to go on developing "birth-control shots" of hormone-ish substances introduced into muscle tissue by hypodermic, which are good for twenty-eight days, or for ninety. And there is the persisting question whether we *can* and whether we *should* change "human nature," with both questions being answered more and more in the affirmative, and more serious doubt always being expressed about the very concept of "human nature" itself.

In all this we must look carefully to our reasoning, not seeing ethical issues where they do not exist, or *failing* to see those that are there. One of Winston Churchill's favorite stories was about the research scientist who pulled off the front legs of a grasshopper and commanded it to jump. It did so. He then pulled off the hind legs and again commanded it to jump. When it failed to move, he wrote in his notes: "Pulling the hind legs off a grasshopper destroys the insect's ability to hear the command 'jump.' "

Is it evil to generate life experimentally in a test tube, and is it murder to end the process once begun? Is it wrong to devise animal-to-human transplants of organs, glands, tissue, as, for example, not only kidneys from baboons, but other material from other animals? Or vice-versa? Or what about blood transfusions drawn from the dead victims of heart attacks, suicide, acute alcoholism, poisoning, or accidents such as electrocution—as they are doing in the Sklifosovsky Institute in Moscow? Is it wrong to permit people to donate organs such as ovaries and kidneys, thus cutting vital function and survival in half? Is it wrong to let a patient die when he could be kept alive by medical means? Or is it wrong to keep patients alive sometimes? Why? Is abortion ever morally licit as a method of birth control, on grounds other than that of pathology and medical indication? Is it wrong to use hallucinogenic drugs—and if so, always or only sometimes? Is it wrong to disclose privileged information and professional secrets to other doctors and paramedical servants of the patient? Is it always wrong to omit explaining a clinical experiment to the patient? These and their like are real and pressing ethical questions.

With such in mind as examples, let us look now at some (not all) recent questions posed by medicine's scientific developments.

The Terror of Conception

Are we prepared to contribute by research and development to the emancipation of people, married and unmarried alike, from the terror of conception? That is the option which the new antinidant pills will offer. The pressure for birth-control medical care for unmarried university students has mounted steadily in recent years. Is it, as some medical men are saying, the physician's duty to help people, not judge them, and to restrict their role to a medical one, not a moral one? Is there any way of understanding what medicine is achieving in birth control, while still hoping that the traditional linkage of lovemaking and baby-making can continue? (I myself think not. The cult of virginity seems to me to be making its last stand against the sexual freedom which medicine has now made possible.)

Another device contributing to fertility control raises an ethical issue as to the nature of the thing rather than as to its use. I mean the intrauterine devices—coils and rings. Probably a majority of Roman Catholic women are already practicing contraception against their church's teaching. But even if they should be freed from that prohibition (which is at least *possible*) they might not be permitted to make use of the much simpler and less expensive IUDs. This all depends on whether conception takes place at fertilization of the ovum, or not until the fertilized zygote has nidated or implanted in the uterus. Here is a question (What is conception?) which has not been fully answered yet by the physiologists and clinicians, some favoring fertilization and some nidation. Which is it? When does pregnancy start? (And incidentally, the answer to this question would also decide whether the so-called morning-after pills are contraceptives or abortifacients.) And behind all this lie the ground questions: "What and when is life?" "What and when is a person?"

Artificial Insemination

There is still a debate going on as to whether artificial insemination from an anonymous donor is adultery or not. The Catholic moralists say it is, because in their view adultery is not intercourse outside the marriage bond but a willing access to any sexual faculty of a person other than one's own spouse. Yet the practice of artificial insemination is carried on by gynecologists increasingly. The courts have reached no clear position as to its legality. It is far less expensive than adoptions, and more easily arranged. When donors are married men with children, their genetic background is more definite than in the case of adopted babies.

Artificial insemination is commonly prescribed after counseling with a couple when the husband is infertile or carries a hereditary disease such as cystic fibrosis, or when he and his wife have incompatible RH blood types which might endanger their child's life. For some childless couples the emotional experience of pregnancy, gestation, and delivery is important. Is this morally objectionable as adultery, or as entailing secrecy or deception, or what? Both jurisprudence and theology find themselves confronted in this matter with a medical development for which they have no adequate account. Is a marriage relationship or a parental relationship validated physiologically only, or can it be authentic on the basis of intention and loving concern?

Indirect Euthanasia

Medical progress in resuscitation and prolonging life have raised the whole ethical problem of what some call indirect euthanasia or anti-dysthanasia. The question is whether we ever have a right to *refrain* from what would keep the patient alive, as distinguished from the classical problem about euthanasia or *doing* something which will end the patient's life. The issue is almost unique in one respect; that is, there is general agreement among theologians that we are not obliged to keep a patient alive by all means possible, regardless of attendant circumstances. But the medical fraternity itself is divided on it. David Karnoffsky of the Sloan-Kettering Institute has said doctors must always do everything they can to prolong life. Vaster numbers are, in practice, of course, treating death as a friend and refusing to stand in its way. But as a people we are culturally confused and contradictory on the subject, and evasive of it. If we practice birth control, why not death control? Why be fatalists in one death and not in the other? And given the comatose condition in which most patients die these days, when indeed *is* death?

Preservation by Freezing

We all have lately read wild tales of cryonics and the use of cryobiology or freezing techniques as a way of preserving a body until a cure is found for some fatal disease suffered by the patient, so that he can be thawed out and treated, and thus cheat death. But what about proposals for the cryonic preservation of sperm and organ banks, or the use of liquid nitrogen to freeze a patient's endometrium as a method of female sterilization (since it causes menstruation to stop)? Is this any more or less a form of temporary sterilization than the steroid pills so widely used these days? Nothing in the ethical tradition prepares modern men to analyze such questions.

In a somewhat lighter vein, I would like to remark that *all* medical developments do not pose such difficult or subtle ethical problems. I am thinking of something I learned about a few years ago in Japan called *jinko shojo*. Women are already practicing deception in cosmetic treatment to straighten noses, remove wrinkles, and even to fill out bust lines (as with silicone). But *jinko shojo* is used by some Japanese gynecologists to create an artificial hymen for prospective brides, either by tightening body tissues or through the use of plastic. One doctor held a party to celebrate his 10,000th *jinko shojo,* saying, "Life is not fair to women." Such a deception is obviously a fraud, but there *is* an ethical problem raised by the kind of double morality which necessitates it.

Use of LSD and psycho-engineering, sex-changing surgically for trans-sexuals (about which some interesting information was made public from the team of surgeons and psychiatrists recently at Johns Hopkins in Baltimore), the apparent eradication of the "sin" of concupiscence when the amygdala of the brain, the passion center, is altered (as by a laser thrust) and a patient changes from nymphomania or satyriasis to a "nice" or virtuous person—all these and similar things raise questions for us morally.

Questions in Social Ethics

We face also questions of *social* ethics. In the first place, it is due to the marvelous successes of medicine that the problem of population pressure looms so large. Medical care, preventive medicine, sanitation—these keep people alive long after their numbers have reached the economically and politically optimum level. Medicine cannot help us to a higher health and longevity rate without facing up to the social issues provoked. Birth control and family planning have to be incorporated in an ethic of population control, or the whole of medicine's development becomes a Frankenstein. We need a contemporary conscience about lovemaking and parenthood. People cannot suppose that they have a right to produce as many children as their desires and resources allow, because the social welfare has to be considered, as well. The affluent family is already a dangerous form of group egoism. What an irony if successful medicine adds to human squalor and misery, as it is actually doing in many lands, and threatens to do even in rich America!

Legal Abortions

The proposals of the American Law Institute for changes in state laws governing legal abortions, proposals aimed at liberalizing the present rather narrow and ungenerous laws, will have to be dealt with by the medical profession. A few medical groups, such as the New York Academy of Medicine, have done so, but for the most part the timidity and conservatism of the medical profession hangs like a sea-anchor over the whole question and frightens timid legislators into running away from the issue, sticking to the superstitious laws of the past seventy-five years.[1] Only medical men have the authority and prestige to move those whose thinking is not primarily rational and constructive. Only doctors can influence the citizenry who live by the conventional wisdom, not realizing how radically unconventional, in the sense of innovative, modern medicine has become.

Social Control of Medicine

How are we to regard the growing social control of medicine (in research, for example) through the Surgeon Gen-

[1] Since this was written, the AMA made a public statement favoring more liberal abortion laws.

eral's office and through the rules laid down for research programs financed by grants from the National Institute of Health? Is it actually possible, for example, to explain to patients what is being done in many research experimental runs, and to get a really competent consent from them? I doubt it, personally. A bill before the New York Assembly severely limiting research on children might be a disaster. The vaccines for polio, measles, and German measles had to be tested on children. Federal programs which require that surgical trainees (residents) be supervised *in situ* by a surgeon-teacher radically reduce the amount of training that can be made available in teaching hospitals. These are examples of the social ethics which affect medical practice, research, and education through the operation of programs like Medicare and Medicaid, and some insurance arrangements.

Think for a moment of the problems posed by the prospect of artificial hearts, either mechanical or prosthetic. Will any stigma be attached to those using artificial hearts? Is there any theological objection? Should manufacturers of artificial hearts be public or private enterprises? What controls should be exerted, and by whom? Who is morally liable if the device fails—the manufacturer, the patient, the hospital and surgeons, or who? In view of the risk of their failure, what about issuing drivers' licenses, for example? Is this any different from the problem of the epileptic? What about the danger to others of radiation from such heart machines if they are fueled with radio-isotopes? Is this danger any worse than smog, water pollution, air traffic overhead? What about the danger to the patient himself? (It is bound to develop some danger after a few years.)

Should such a heart with, say, forty percent of isotope life still left be transferred by autopsy to a living person in need of it? What if biological death comes and the heart goes on beating? Is the person dead? (Clinical death is almost "old hat" already because of the new resuscitation procedures.) Is such a device worth it for only two or three years? Is it worth it for ten years, if leukemia results from radiation? Suppose a patient says "No"—is that suicide? If the patient is beyond competent decision, who decides, and why?

Bordering more closely upon purely professional ethics than anything I have mentioned yet, but still of social import, are three matters I should like to see worked out in ethical coherence: One is the organization and profitable operation of pharmacies by physicians whose names do not appear on their plates or prescription slips, but to which patients are sent for supplies. Another is the prescription of drugs by their expensive trade names instead of their inexpensive generic name. (Generic prednisone, for example, sells for $2.95, but under the trade name Meticorten its sale price is $19.95.) This kind of thing reminds us, doesn't it, that prescriptions were put into Latin and kept there as much as anything to hide what they say from the patient! And it is sad that these two ethical questions have not been dealt with by the AMA, so that a senate investigating committee has had to take them up.

The third thing, and very explosive it is in terms of emotion, is the medical boycott or strike. What does this tell us, in its growing frequency, about what is happening to the classical concept of a guild for professional medical people? And one thinks in this connection of more than mass boycotts; for what are we to say ethically when doctors simply refuse to respond to calls? Consider the case of two doctors who were the only ones available in a small Florida town, who recently served notice that they will no longer practice obstetrics, thus forcing patients either to go as far as fifty miles for delivery or else to be delivered by mid-wives. These ethical issues are signs of our times.

Finally, as a question in the social ethics of medical care, how responsible is it to spend huge sums of money for relatively isolated life-prolonging devices such as renal dialysis and cardio-prosthetic materials, at a time when infant and neo-natal morbidity and mortality in many ghetto areas are at such shockingly high levels?

In Conclusion

Scientific and technological advances in medicine are raising new ethical problems, and old problems in new forms. Many of them are "normative" problems, problems about what we value and why and in what relative order or priority, in contrast to such critical questions as to whether an IUD is abortifacient or not. We are in a crisis of human affairs provoked by medicine. Not just *how* we may do things or even *what* things we do, but *why!* It is at this point of "metaethics" that religious faith or the lack of it has a decisive bearing.

Man may soon be free of hunger and infectious diseases. People may enjoy a vigorous mental and physical life until ninety or one hundred. Defective parts of the body are already being replaced, even prenatally, in theory. Medicine's staggering power over human genetics and health is the source of it all. It is a success problem, not a failure problem.

Whether it is done by surgery (as in leucotomic), or by ESB (electrical stimulation of the brain, as in the Soviet sleep machine), or chemically (as with mind-changers like the hallucinogens, for example LSD), or however it's done, the "medical cyborg" is here, a human being repaired or reinforced by artificial devices. The *amplified* man is a form of the "extension of man" not yet even recognized by Marshall McLuhan with all his talk about communication and the mass media!

Let me come to an end. I offer four concluding assertions:

1) Technology is the source of our most searching and reconstructive problems in ethics. This is the age of control—the era of cybernetics—the epoch of the transistor, or of the control of control. And classical Christian theology is simply not equipped conceptually to cope with it. Christians can't even ask the right questions any more!

2) Every increase in our power of control over life and health and death, over the conditions of human existence, can be hubristic as well as agapeic, used for evil as well as for good; or as our rabbinical brothers might say, *yetzer ra* or *yetzer tov*. This is the paradox of freedom or, if you prefer, of moral status. But I personally am not a know-nothing Christian. I believe that the old adage is sound—*abusus non tollit usum*—the abuse of a thing does not bar its use. All of medicine and bio-engineering is an interference with nature, using it or bypassing it for humanly chosen ends. No sound Christian anthropology will limit men to the order of nature. Grace or freedom, with all its grave risks when seriously accepted, is the first-order principle of all morality.

3) I believe that we must stop talking about "human nature." It is a prescientific and pre-technological concept, now discredited.

4) We can see that while technology and science solve many human problems, they also create new problems in the very process of solving the old ones. *To solve these problems we must not and cannot abandon our technology; we have to use more of it.* Having bitten into the fruit of the tree of knowledge, we cannot return to Eden. We have reached the end of innocence.

VI. Toward Continuing Dialogue

Roy Nichols
Amos N. Johnson
Howard J. Clinebell, Jr.

Roy Nichols

My statement will center on the practical matters that relate to the minister and the physician in their everyday area of operation where medicine and theology need a more understanding personal association.

Predisposing Professional Considerations

The minister in a typical American church is a general practitioner. During a given day, he may include in the course of his duties both the horizontal and vertical extremities of human existence. An infant baptism, a funeral, listening to a distressed husband or wife, rejoicing with newlyweds, wrestling with a dissident teen-ager, talking with an auto mechanic, sweeping the floor of his study, running the mimeograph machine, trying to be a father to a family—all belong to his responsibilities.

Only the general practitioner in the medical profession, serving a small-town clientele, approximates the scope of the minister's personal engagements in a given day. For this reason, the medical general practitioner presents the most likely place to succeed in bridging the gap that now divides the two primary agents in the health and healing ministry of the community. Of course, social workers and other professionals have a tremendous influence on healing ministries, and we should not forget them.

The variable background and training may present a barrier between the minister as a general practitioner and the medical man as a general practitioner, in some instances. In most states, the qualifications of doctors are rigidly determined by state laws and governing boards. In the ministry, such a universal guarantee is not possible. This suggests that any realistic negotiation between ministers and medical men must begin on a selective basis.

While the education of the clergy and the doctor is a major factor in the success of such encounters, readiness, desire, and sophistication are also important factors. Each man must begin with a profound appreciation for the work of the other, and the realization of the oneness of their health and healing endeavor under God.

The potential barrier of the economic status of the minister and the doctor is significant. It is, in part, responsible for certain latent resentments and feelings of condescension, but we must succeed within the context of this unequal association, without permitting the status factors to prevent us from joining hands in the work that we must do.

Practically, at the local level, we can begin with the following elemental steps:

1. Doctors might invite interested ministers to accompany them as silent partners on a hospital round, just to get the feel of a doctor's view of the patient.

2. Ministers might arrange to use the professional abilities of the doctor in church discussion groups, rather than on boards of trustees, dealing with the constant issues involving the health and happiness of persons in the community.

3. Doctors might suggest to patients that they consult with certain ministers, recognizing, of course, that a doctor

cannot invade the privacy of his patients by making such a suggestion unless there is an obvious readiness on the part of the patient.

4. Ministers might refer patients to certain doctors, because of their feeling of affinity with that certain doctor. While this might seem like professional back scratching, if that's where we itch, then let's get at it.

Preliminary conversations might result in fruitful, practical approaches to cooperation that meet the real requirements of both groups of professionals. It is very difficult in a conference like this to project just how in a particular community doctors and preachers can begin negotiations in a workable way. Maybe this has to start in conversations and then begin from that point to find practical answers and further steps.

Professional Confidences

Both the medical men and the ministers are constantly involved in critical confidential information and experiences. Both the doctors and the preachers are ethically bound to keep these secrets. Within the orbit of professional association, however, ministers and doctors have the opportunity of consulting, if they have confidence in each other. In fact, some of the monumental decisions we have discussed in this conference concerning the application of medical techniques might be more adequately handled if ministers and doctors had an open line of confidential communication between them.

We must, however, learn to trust and respect each other; in fact, I consider this the primary barrier which, over the years, has divided us.

Responsibility of Seminaries and Medical Schools

In theological seminaries we have not taken seriously our responsibility to provide the kind of orientation that causes the graduates of the seminaries and the medical schools to anticipate a working relationship with each other. Some theological seminaries, interested in the training of prospective ministers in counseling, have utilized the services of psychiatrists. I do not know of a non-Catholic medical school where serious consideration is given to either theological or ministerial involvement in the work of the medical man.

The long history of controversy between science and religion has constructed a wall of fear, and even though the reasons for the wall are no longer valid, the wall still exists. My recommendation is this: The undergraduate preparation of every minister should include some of the biological sciences, and every seminary should provide courses in which practicing medical doctors may involve theological students in the physical aspect of the health and healing ministry.

Similarly, every medical school should begin to provide some serious courses, taught by a practicing minister, perhaps in the senior year or at some stage in internship, that would give medical men a kind of readiness for ministerial and medical cooperation at the community level when they graduate. Across the country, in many medical schools, this is being done with reference to medical training and social work, because the social work profession, in an organized way, has pushed this collaboration. Most medical doctors, especially now with involvements in medical care and hospitalization plans, as well as public medical services, find it necessary to have some knowledge of the work of the professional social worker as it interacts with the medical profession.

The Hospital as a Training Center

Where hospital chaplains are adequately prepared to assume leadership, and where they possess the spirit and desire to do so, they remain extremely important links in converting the hospital into a training center where working relationships between the clergy and the medical men may be developed. In cooperation with the medical staff, experiences can be arranged so that selected parish ministers, and selected medical men, may meet at the point of the hospital's working operation. Such experiences as sitting in on consultations as a silent partner, observing surgery, and listening to the words of the surgeon as he goes through his work are very helpful. Permitting a minister to address the medical staff on matters relevant to the medical and ministerial link of cooperation is useful. Some hospitals are already busily engaged in such experiments, but the instances need to be multiplied.

Faith Healing and Health

Some ministers have developed a consuming interest in what we commonly call "divine healing," as if there were a difference between that kind of healing and some other. All healing is divine. If healing services are conducted in the context of worship, where prayer and the laying on of hands are employed to relieve the sick, we are extending the oldest ministry of the church. I am conversant with at least one instance where this is effectively done, in Foundry Methodist Church in Washington, D.C. There an extremely adequate and well-worked-out program of healing and health therapy is provided under ideal spiritual circumstances in the church, with the cooperation and the participation of the medical profession.

But exclusive healing services antagonistic to the ministry of the medical doctor, who is also involved in the healing ministry, ignore the fullest meaning of divine healing. God is ministering to the health of man through many agencies. The so-called physical doctor and the so-called spiritual doctor are ineffective if they are isolated and estranged from each other.

The Moral Circumstance

Modern medicine, by its own admission, is confused as to the proper application of its professional skills and abilities. Theologians also are uncertain about the relevance of certain ancient principles to the practical affairs of a modern age. Perhaps providentially, this is the ideal circumstance and climate in which we can come together to meet each other in true humility. There is one God, one universe, and one family of man. As leaders in both the medical and ministerial professions, our task is to interpret the basis of harmony and health to our people. The line of division between the sacred and the secular must be erased.

Now we must join hands and continue the journey toward fulfillment which began when God first placed man and woman in the Garden of Eden. We are finite creatures, limited in our comprehension, even of the simplest aspects of our lives. This is fact. But we are here in this conference because God has revealed to us a new word, in Jesus Christ.

We believe that the excitement of health, for both the rich and the poor alike, can come and will come to us through the message and ministry of our Lord Jesus Christ, and we are his agents. If we will labor together, controlled by disciplines that he set forth for us, we are certain to discover the abundant life which he promised.

Amos N. Johnson

I would like to speak in the first part of my summary of the concept that is becoming accepted rather widely all over the United States: health as a community affair. We are seeing certain communities, identifiable throughout this country, that are facing up to this. These communities are organizing nonprofit corporations, and they are expending a considerable amount of time and money in planning the comprehensive health care of their communities.

Health Is a Community Affair

In each of these communities we identify several subcommunities. First, we must include the community of governments. If the area is large, it may be a county government. If it is small, it may be a municipal government. Then we identify the governmental agencies, such as public health, welfare, the hospitals and the clinics, that are paid for by government funds.

We also identify in these communities the Christian congregation. That includes the clergy, the Christian hospitals, the church volunteers, and other identifiable groups that are working with health matters from the orientation of religion.

Then we have the medical and the paramedical personnel,

the doctors, the nurses, the public health nurses, the laboratory technicians, the social workers, and so on.

We also have the categorical social groups that exist in most communities to provide medical services, and we identify those as the Cancer Society, the Arthritis Foundation, the Mental Health Society, Muscular Distrophy, and others.

And, lastly, we have the total community, which is an interested citizenry. This is of the essence. I believe that more and more people in this country are now beginning to become vitally interested in their total health picture.

Clergy and Physicians Coordinate Community Effort

The real finding of this conference is that the clergy and the physicians must be the motivators and coordinators of this community effort, as well as the purveyors of individualized and personalized specific services. We need to establish, at a local level, plans for the implementation of community medical concern. We recognize a mutual interdependence among all the organizations that have been identified, and particularly a mutual interdependence between the physician and the minister. So we should be getting about the matter of involving every community, every medical society, every Christian congregation in this country in the business of working for total medical care for everyone regardless of financial ability to pay, or of color, race, or creed.

We Need a Common Definition of Health

Let us identify some of our problems. First, I think that we have to identify a concept of health which we can all understand and about which we can all talk with a common language. Medicine has a tendency to develop its own peculiar language. I understand that the ministry has some tendency that way itself. So we need to identify and get together on a mutually understandable language.

Health, we may say, is a relative state of well-being, as assessed at a given point in time, which relates to the four identifiable components of the whole man:

Man is spiritual; man is physical; man is social; man is emotional. Each component is intimately and inseparably entwined with the others, and the whole person is greater than the total of these components. A state of good health exists at any time when these four components are in balance at a high level of normal function. When any one of these four components develops abnormal functions or complaints, the whole man becomes sick. It matters not whether the disease (or dis-ease) has its origin in emotional upset, organic or functional physical disorders, social maladjustment, or spiritual problems. The entire man reacts adversely to this illness. The primary offending component in any such illness is difficult to isolate for specific, effective diagnosis and treatment. We cannot set about to take one component of a person and identify this as the single component that is essential to the treatment if the whole man is to be made totally well.

Comprehensive Health Care

Therefore, it follows that the maintenance of a state of good health and well-being for this man requires *health* care, not simply medical care. When I speak of medical care as opposed to health care, I am thinking of what happened to the concept of medical care during our scientific explosion since 1910 and the Abrams-Flexner report, which revolutionized medical education, medical research, and the delivery of medical services to the people in this country, and started the business of specialization. I am not opposed to this or to any of the services I have mentioned. They have been productive of the highest quality of medical care that is available in almost any country on this globe. But somewhere along the line the pendulum has swung from medical education producing morons to the production now of medical spastics. I do not know which is of more service to mankind.

Let us determine what we mean by health care. Comprehensive health care may be regarded as having two components: a service component and a function component. The services may be again divided down into essential components; these essential components are: 1) normal development, which represents primary preventive health services; 2) the containment of those diseases that chronically beset mankind, and remedial care, which is of the essence but not of the ninety-five percent essence that we now see in the total medical care picture; 3) rehabilitation.

1. *Normal Development.* The need for services to assure normal development goes without saying. This requires that physical facilities and atmosphere be available in every community for all persons, children, adolescents, young married couples, older couples, retired, and the very old, conducive to their normal development and productivity. This is the essence of prospective preventive medicine. It is quite a new concept and quite radical, and it is difficult for some people to understand it, but I think that we are working toward it.

Medicine and religion owe it to their communities to see that it is available for all people. That includes food, recreation, cultural pursuits, and so on.

2. *Chronic Illness.* Nor can we ignore the chronically ill. Very little interest has been shown in this country in the rendering of medical care to people with arthritis, diabetes, and those other chronic diseases that stay with us throughout life, once they are initiated in our bodies.

3. *Rehabilitation.* A patient should start rehabilitation the day he becomes ill, in some instances even before he becomes ill. Rehabilitation is not just the matter of getting a person where he can use an arm again, or take a step with a drag and shuffle if he has had a cerebral vascular accident. There must be a rehabilitation of the emotions, rehabilitation of their adjustment to society, and rehabilitation of the facilities to which these people go home to spend the rest of their lives. They should have facilities on the ground floor, without scatter rugs which are apt to trip and break up old people, and they should be rehabilitated to productivity if at all possible.

The Family Is the Target Group

In the concept of total health care, the family is the target group. The attempt throughout the last ten or twenty years to render medical and health care to people in this country as categorical groups has broken down. You cannot render health care to people over sixty-five years of age any more than you can render health care categorically to people under one year of age, or categorically to those who have muscular dystrophy, or categorically to those who have diabetes. Health care is a broad picture. We must render services to all members of the family. We must know the entire family and must know how each individual relates to the family.

We should also identify the need to have a working agreement among a group of specialists in an area. Every family physician will not be able to treat every disease that besets mankind. We recognize that some twenty or thirty percent of the unusual and the bizarre diseases require referral to someone who has been trained in depth. This we expect to do, and the family physician should have his group practice without walls between him and the specialists to whom he refers his patients.

We should also use our computers. We should be trained and astute in observing our community of patients, each member of our family. Over a period of thirty-three years I have put on my computer all the available facts, social, economic, whatever, about my entire community of patients. The minute one of them comes into my office I have an instant recall, a whole picture of his life, even further back, his father and mother, his grandparents, and so on. What does this do? This enables me, or any other family physician, to detect at the earliest moment any variance from the normal in any member of our community of patients. We can detect, when one of our patients comes in for a sore throat, that one or two of the smaller joints are getting a bit large and the patient cannot use his hand readily. That is the earliest sign of arthritis. We detect many little things of that nature if we are astute. That enables us to supply better-quality medical care.

About specialization and the provision of medical care to the whole person, I would like to quote Aldous Huxley: "The fox knows many things, but the hedgehog knows one big thing." The family physician, to supply medical care to the total man, has to be a fox. The specialist may well be a respectable hedgehog.

Howard J. Clinebell, Jr.

Interprofessional Bridges Now Exist

What we have been doing here together has been to work at pulling down old walls, which have tended to separate the minister and the physician, strengthening some of the bridges which already exist, and building some new bridges that need to be constructed.

What are some of the bridges which already exist?

First, doctors, ministers, and paramedical people share a concern for wholeness which we now recognize must include the meanings of life. Man lives in his meanings, and if this factor is omitted from the equation, we have left the humanness out of humanity. We are all concerned about the alleviation of suffering; suffering we cause by our mistakes, and suffering caused by the processes of nature and by accidents. This common concern for the suffering of the people to whom we minister in our several professions is a deep bond. The loneliness of suffering is one of the most intense forms of loneliness, and it is one of the times in life when we most need one another and the coordinated help of professionals who share a deep concern about people.

Second, I think we have a common bridge already present in our effort to keep the personal from being squeezed out by pressure of time and technical concerns. This is not just a problem for doctors. All of us who are aware of the power of the personal know the multiple ways in which it gets squeezed out of us in the hectic pace of our professional activities in whatever setting.

Third, I believe that we share a common link in the recognition that both professions involve combinations of technical skills and artistry. This has been emphasized, and it is most obvious in connection with medicine; but it is also true of the ministry.

Fourth, there are the common problems of specialization in both professions. The searching paper by Doctor Casberg raised the issue for medicine. Many of the same issues should be raised for the ministry. As an aside, it is noteworthy that some of the most significant interprofessional communication has occurred between practitioners of medicine and the new specialists in the ministry—the chaplain-supervisors and the pastoral counseling specialists. The reason for this, I suspect, is that these clergymen have had clinical training and have had considerable practice in interprofessional dialogue.

Fifth, I think that both groups of professionals share a common need for new guidelines. Both of us are equally confused about many of the new ethical issues that Dr. Fletcher so expertly called to our attention.

Sixth, we both deal with the results of alienation and depend on many of the same forces in healing. The concept of alienation is a window-opener, in terms of understanding the whole phenomenon of mental, emotional, spiritual, and social illness. Man is alienated by guilt, anxiety, estrangement, loneliness, and dishonesty. All of us are dependent, in the healing process, on the forces of reconciliation, the forces of grace, love, honesty, and hope.

And finally, we both are joined, whether we know it or

not, by our common danger of the misuse of the power that society has invested in us. Ministers and doctors are members of "omnipotence professions"—the professions to which the public ascribes certain powers of a nonrational sort. The danger of misuse of these powers is great if we allow ourselves to incorporate such feelings of power into our professional self-images.

Strengthening the Bridges

These bridges of common problems and concerns already exist. They need to be strengthened and used more fully. The whole explosion in the field of mental health and psychosomatic medicine, as Doctor Braceland pointed out, provides us with not only an opportunity for greater cooperation, but new channels for this cooperation. When one looks around the country and sees what has happened in community mental health, the explosion of activity on every level, one must ask the question: "Where is the church? Have we missed the challenge? Have we seen the vision of the healing Christ in this new explosion of interest in mental health?" The mental health revolution is the concern of every churchman. It is a revolution in which the church must become more involved both because it deals with human values and because the church has a contribution to make.

New bridges of cooperation can and should be built between the ministry and the health disciplines on three levels:

First, better bridges of theory are essential, i.e., understanding the nature of health in the light of the answer to the greater and prior question of the nature of man. The concept of wholeness is probably the most helpful single concept for understanding our common task. It is a bridge concept between professions. Wholeness is on the same continuum as salvation. Our speakers have done us a great service in pointing to the need for building these bridges of theoretical understanding, and indicating some of the materials by which the bridges can and will be built.

A part of the bridge of theory which we now possess only in part is an understanding of the unique role of each profession. We need to respect each other's respective areas of competence. Even more, we need to understand the areas where our competences may overlap. This is primarily in the area of the psychological dimension of man and in interpersonal relationships. The minister's unique contribution adheres in his training, in the fact that he has systematically studied theology, philosophy, comparative religion, psychology of religion, and ethics. It adheres in his use of religious tools. I suspect that most if not all of us are in agreement with Dr. Hiltner that all healing is spiritual; yet it seems that the church may have a special responsibility for defining the guidelines in those types of healing which employ modalities that are primarily nonmedical. Those of you who came to this meeting with a primary concern in what usually is meant by the term "spiritual healing" may feel a bit shortchanged by what has transpired here. Perhaps we ministers tend to deemphasize our interest in spiritual healing (through the use of religious modalities), in meetings like this one, because of uneasiness about what the doctors will think. Can our relationships interprofessionally become deep enough to allow us to talk productively and honestly about our differences?

This leads to the second kind of bridges which we need—the communication bridges. We need to learn to communicate more effectively with each other, particularly on touchy topics, such as euthanasia (whether it is performed by a positive act of decision or by simply stopping certain procedures).

Communication is the instrument by which we can resolve differences and learn to work together more effectively. Communication has another value, that of giving mutual support and sustenance to those engaged in meaningful interaction. To illustrate, I believe that one of the values that doctors can fulfill is that of being pastors to pastors. Being a professional of any kind can pose problems of loneliness. The problem is that of having a plethora of contacts and a poverty of real relationships. Friendships between doctors and ministers often have a mutually supportive and beneficial effect.

The third type of bridge which is needed is practice bridges formed by working together on the same "human documents." For example, when a parishioner feeds back to the minister the juicy bit of information that the psychiatrist to whom the minister had referred him is "only interested in sex," or is "against religion," the minister should check this out with the doctor to see what he had in mind. Otherwise cooperation will be short-lived. Meaningful communication will be enhanced if the doctor is willing and able to think theologically about medical decisions, and if the pastor is willing and able to think scientifically about the pastoral care of persons. If we want cooperation we must understand enough of the other profession's language, philosophy, and goals to keep the lines of communication open.

Methods of Cooperation

In summary, let me suggest certain methods for facilitating cooperation:

1. Ministers need clinical training to prepare them for full cooperation. Theological education, at long last, is grasping the significance of the internship principle in professional education. Through clinical training, ministers learn to communicate with doctors, to feel comfortable in a hospital setting, and to work effectively with persons in crisis.

2. We need cross-frontier experiences in professional education. Our seminaries ought to have a psychiatrist, general practitioner, or surgeon in residence for several weeks each year. Medical schools might well have theologians in residence for limited periods. Even better are regular seminars in which medical and theological students wrestle together, under the leadership of a doctor and a minister, with common concerns.

3. Those who are in the parish ministry and in hospital chaplaincies can come up with their own models of creative interprofessional bridge-building. The key is depth interaction, opportunities for dialogue in depth. I would suggest the retreat principle as one possibility; or the lay academy principle, where people get together and knock heads for several days running and get down to the gut-level issues. We need to face differences, become willing to talk about where we differ radically as well as where we agree. The "pastoral care team" idea is another way of bridge-building and at the same time implementing the pastorhood of all believers. Through such teams doctors and other professional persons and laymen can find their style of personal ministry. A pastoral care team is simply a small group of

people within a congregation who are given special training by the pastor and by the mental health and medical disciplines within the church, in ministering to the bereaved, to the family of the mentally ill, the family of the alcoholic, to the lonely, etc. This is a fresh conception of ministry that has all kinds of possibilities for enhancing the church's person-centered work.

4. Denominational bridge-building is certainly needed. Our church might well appoint an ongoing task force including some of the best minds from the medical, the nursing, the social work, the theological and ministerial ranks, to work out the implications of what we have done here, and to come up with position papers which will help to plan strategy for implementation as well as inform those who are interested in the denomination.

5. Finally, we should build bridges on an ecumenical basis wherever possible. Exciting things are happening in the area of healing on the levels of both the National Council of Churches and World Council of Churches. To work with persons of similar concerns in other churches and across faith and national lines is crucial.

Proposals for Action

In the light of this, I would like to make these proposals for action:

First, that a conference of this type be held centering on the ethical problems of contemporary medicine. Here we have split the focus between pastoral-care concerns and ethical concerns. We need a conference devoted exclusively to medical ethics in the age of technology.

Second, we need a listing of what is actually being done

around the country in facilitating communication across professional lines. For example, at the University of Chicago Divinity School there is an ongoing seminar on ministry to the terminal patient, involving both medical students and theological students. Behind a one-way mirror they observe terminally ill patients being interviewed. This is a creative approach and is the kind of thing that ought to be happening all over the country and made known to us, so that we can learn from and be inspired by the experience of others.

Third, each of us has an obligation to become a committee of one to implement, in his own style and in his own local situation, physician-clergy cooperation.

And finally, the decision-makers of our denominations should develop policy statements or ethical guidelines on matters such as suicide, abortion, prolongation of life, organ transplant, and other areas involving complex human values.

The members of one of our work groups have stated the theological basis for clergy-doctor cooperation: "Wherever men are working for wholeness and health, there God is working. As Christians, we are to join Him in that work, whatever our vocation may be." This is the deepest basis of our common concern and the fundamental reason why we must continue to join our hands in the name of Him who was called "Great Physician."

A CLOSING PRAYER

Almighty God, our Father, we are grateful for these days, days which came from Thee even as all our days have come, days we have been privileged to spend together. We are grateful for this single day, this solitary hour in which we live, and for the many blessings it has brought us. We are grateful for the aspiring mind of man which probes the mysteries of science to the reaches of an infinite universe. But we would acknowledge, even as we carry to the ends of the earth and to the humblest of Thy children the products of man's search, the benefits of his discoveries, that we carry also the power to annihilate and the keys to destroy.

We would aspire to a deeper sense of compassion, to a greater concern for those less privileged than we; and we would seek always the sustaining and uplifting power of Thy great love and compassion.

And now, unto Him who is able to keep you from falling and present you faultless before the presence of His glory with exceeding joy, to the only wise God our Saviour, be glory and majesty, dominion and power, both now and evermore. Amen.

RAYMOND D. PRUITT

SELECTED BIBLIOGRAPHY

Key References

Healing Church, The. Report on the Tübingen Consultation, 1964. Geneva: World Council of Churches, 1965. (Used as preparatory material for the Rochester Convocation.)

Relation of Christian Faith to Health, The. Report adopted by the 172nd General Assembly of the United Presbyterian Church in the United States of America, May 1960. Board of National Missions, 475 Riverside Drive, New York. (Used as preparatory material for the Rochester Convocation.)

Sharpe, W. D. *Medicine and the Ministry: A Medical Basis for Pastoral Care.* New York: The Meredith Publishing Company, 1966.

Tournier, Paul. *The Healing of Persons.* New York: Harper & Row, 1965. Dr. Tournier shows how the personal problems of the patient, his relationships with family, with friends, with the world, and with God can be contributing factors to physical illness. Through the sharing of himself and his Christian faith he leads patients to make changes in their ways of living that often lead to increased physical well-being. In his own person he demonstrates the immense value of pastor-physician teamwork.

Additional References Pertinent to the Convocation

1. *Pastor-Physician, Ministry-Medicine Relationships.*

Dicks, Russell L. *Who Is My Patient? A Religious Manual for Nurses.* New York: The Macmillan Company, 1941.

Frankl, Viktor E. *The Doctor and the Soul.* Trans. by Richard and Clara Winston. New York: Alfred A. Knopf, 1955.

Garlick, Phyllis L. *Man's Search for Health: A Study in the Inter-Relation of Religion and Medicine.* London: Highway Press, 1952.

Gladston, Iago, ed. *Ministry and Medicine in Human Relationships.* New York: International Universities Press, 1955.

Jackson, Douglas MacG. "The Personal Approach to the Patient," *Journal of the Christian Medical Association of India* (September, 1962), pp. 435-40.

Jenkins, Daniel T., ed. *The Doctor's Profession.* London: SCM Press, 1949. An enlightened theological analysis of the physician's work by an English Congregational minister.

Lister, John. "Statement of Need for Mutual Understanding Between Doctors and Clergy," *New England Journal of Medicine* (1954), p. 193.

Robinson, G. Canby. *The Patient as a Person.* New York: Commonwealth Fund, 1939.

Scott, William R. "Potentials for Ministry in Medical Work," *Journal of the Christian Medical Association of India* (November, 1959), pp. 352-57.

Southard, Samuel. *Religion and Nursing.* Nashville: Broadman Press, 1959.

Westberg, Granger E. "The Hospital Chaplain's Contribution to Physician-Clergy Cooperation," *The Pharos* (October, 1959), pp. 217-21, 240.

Westberg, Granger, E. *Nurse, Pastor, and Patient.* Rock Island: Augustana Press, 1955.

2. *The Community and Mental Health.*

Lambourne, R. A. *Community, Church and Healing.* London: Darton, Longman and Tood, 1963.

Scherzer, Carl J. *The Church and Healing.* Philadelphia: The Westminster Press, 1950.

Taylor, John V. "The Healing Community," *CMS Newsletter,* No. 277 (December, 1964).

Westberg, Granger E. *Community Psychiatry and the Clergyman.* Springfield, Ill.: Charles C. Thomas, 1966.

3. *Ethical Issues.*

Edmunds, Vincent, and Scorer, Gordon, eds. *Ideals in Medicine: A Christian Approach to Medical Practice.* London: The Tyndale Press, 1958.

Fletcher, J. *Situation Ethics: The New Morality.* Philadelphia: The Westminster Press, 1966.

Garceau, O. "Morals of Medicine." Bibliography, Annals of the American Academy, 363:60-69 (January, 1966).

Hayes, Edward J., Hayes, Paul J., and Kelley, Dorothy Ellen. *Moral Handbook of Nursing.* New York: The Macmillan Company, 1956.

Stumpf, S. E. "Some Moral Dimensions of Medicine," *Annals of Internal Medicine,* 64: No. 2 (February, 1966).

Taylor, C. E. "Ethics for an International Health Profession." Bibliography, *Science,* 153:716-20 (August 12, 1966).

Wolfensberger, W. "Ethical Issues in Research with Human Subjects." Bibliography, *Science,* 155:47-51 (January 6, 1967).

4. *General References.*

Bálint, Michael. *The Doctor, His Patient and the Illness.* New York: International Universities Press, 1957.

Belgum, David. *Clinical Training for Pastoral Care.* Philadelphia: The Westminster Press, 1956.

Braceland, Francis J., ed. *Faith, Reason and Modern Psychiatry.* New York: P. J. Kenedy and Sons, 1955.

Casberg, M. A. "Knowledge Comes, but Wisdom Lingers," *Journal of Medical Education,* 33:686-95 (September, 1958).

Doniger, Simon, ed. *Healing: Human and Divine.* New York: Association Press, 1957.

Field, Minna. *Patients Are People: A Medical-Social Approach to Prolonged Illness.* New York: Columbia University Press, 1958.

Kavanaugh, Kiernan, O.C.D. "LSD and Religious Experience, a Theologian's Viewpoint," *Spiritual Life* (Spring, 1967).

Mach, René, "Médicine scientifique et respect de la personne," *Journal de Genève* (September, 1952).

Neubauer, Vinzenz, "Der Weg zur Persönlichkeit." Innsbruck, Vienna: Tyrolia Verlag, 1947.

Standard, Samuel, and Nathan, Helmuth, eds. *Should the Patient Know the Truth?* New York: Springer Publishing Co., 1955.

Szilagyi, D. E. "In Defense of the Art of Medicine," *Archives of Surgery,* 91:708-9 (November, 1965).

Tillich, Paul. "The Relation of Religion and Health: Historical Considerations and Theoretical Questions," *Review of Religion,* X, 4 (May, 1946), 348-84.

Tournier, Paul, *The Meaning of Persons.* New York: Harper & Row, 1957.

Tournier, Paul, *The Person Reborn,* trans. by Edwin Hudson. New York: Harper & Row, 1966.

Westberg, Granger E. "Advice to the Family on Being Given Diagnosis of Cancer," *The Medical Clinics of North America* (March, 1958).

"What the Patient Felt: Personal Papers," *Lancet,* 1:361 (February, 1966).

5. *Bibliographies.*

Healing Church, The. Report on the Tübingen Consultation, 1964. Geneva: World Council of Churches, 1965, pp. 50-53.

Relation of Christian Faith to Health, The. United Presbyterian Church Board of Missions (May, 1960), 475 Riverside Drive, New York, pp. 65-74.

"Selected Bibliography on Medical Missions," in *Occasional Bulletin of the Missionary Research Library,* Vol. XV, No. 4. Available from the Medical Research Library, 3041 Broadway, New York.

Westberg, Granger E., "Tentative Bibliography: the Relationship of Health and Religion," the University of Chicago. Available from the American Medical Association, Department of Medicine and Religion, 535 North Dearborn St., Chicago.

See also articles by O. Garceau, C. E. Taylor, and W. Wolfensberger, listed above.